C000041339

deptford creek surviving regeneration

edited by Jess Steele

Published by
Deptford Forum Publishing
441 New Cross Road
London SE14 6TA
0181 692 7115

On behalf of Jill Goddard
Lewisham Environmental Projects Co-ordinator
Creekside Office
60 McMillan Street
London SE8 3HA
0181 312 5515

All profits from sales of this publication will go to the new Deptford Creek Educational Trust
and help towards the running of the Floating Education Centre.

Editor and Project Manager   Jess Steele
Editorial assistant   Portia Smith
Designer   Penny@ META:Language
Printed by   Signal Press Ltd

With assistance from Roy Florentine and Peter Hill of *Cyber* CDP

© Deptford Forum Publishing, 1999

This publication draws together the findings of over 20 separate surveys. The rights of the surveyors to be identified as
the authors of the surveys have been established by them in accordance with the Copyright, Designs & Patents Act 1988.

ISBN 1 898536 76 7
British Library Cataloguing-in-Publication Data
A catalogue record for this publication is available from the British Library

contents

acknowledgements

This book, which brings together information from many sources, including 21 specialist surveys, could not have been written without true partnership and the diverse contributions of many individuals and organisations. Many of the surveyors and other advisers have attended numerous meetings, rewritten and extended the survey text where necessary, donated photographs and spent hours discussing the format. The publishing team have also worked extremely hard to turn varied and highly technical surveys into the book we all wanted to see and, in the process, taught us something about publishing.

I would like to thank the following people and organisations:

- Nick Bertrand & John O'Reilly – Conservation Works and Lewisham Group London Wildlife Trust
- Mike Canty – local marine designer/surveyor of the Creek's 'unwanted objects'
- Jonathan Ducker – Assistant Project Manager, Creek Environment Project
- Dusty Gedge – local ornithologist
- Richard A Jones – local entomologist
- Mike Paice – local ornithologist
- Ken Whittaker – English Heritage
- Mathew Frith – London Wildlife Trust
- John Archer – London Ecology Unit
- Dr David Gaimster – British Museum
- Dr Märit Gaimster – archaeologist
- Environment Agency staff
- Dr Chris Phillpotts – archaeologist
- Dr Iain Boulton & Joanna Kollek – University of Greenwich
- Marcus Trett and his staff – Physalia Ltd
- Gillian King & Simon Mason – Museum of London Archaeological Service
- Ian Titley & Eileen J Cox – Natural History Museum
- Graham Marshall – Urban Initiatives
- Miles Delap – Robert West Consulting
- Dr Nick Carter and his staff – British Trust for Ornithology
- Paul Sinadurai – English Nature
- Richard Walker – Deptford Discovery Team/Groundwork
- Pete Pope – Co oPepys/Deptford Discovery Team
- Julian Kingston & Jeannie Seymour – local boatowners
- Mark Seaman – Mowlem

Final thanks to Don Waders and everyone who has attended a Creekside Environment Open Meeting since they began in August 1996.

Jill Goddard, December 1998

editor's preface

"Deep, deep down in Deptford Creek,
Lies a treasure hard to seek,
If you look there you will find,
Something that will blow your mind!"
– adapted by local children from the 1939 dance hit, 'The Deptford Dip'

It is well-known that London is a city of neighbourhoods; it is just as true that it is riven with borderlands, places whose identities are unofficial and therefore unrecognised. These are places which fall between the structures of local government and become 'forgotten parishes'. Ignored by officialdom, they harbour those forces which care nothing for borders – tides, wildlife, dereliction, rubbish, hope.

Deptford Creek, the tidal section of the River Ravensbourne, is one of these places. Snaking from Deptford Bridge to the Thames and collecting water from an urban area of some 113 square kilometres, the Creek is an integral part of London's flood defences. It is also a wild space with a glorious diversity of 'users' from the tiniest algae to the majestic kestrel. The Creek is special because of its abandonment by humans. Industrial decline and neglect were the very basis for recovery, offering an opportunity for wildlife communities to colonise.

This is why 'renewal' can be an ominous word. The surveyors whose work is synthesised in this publication, caught the Creek at a moment when it was more diverse and robust than it had been for a century. It is not only the Creek channel which is important; the adjacent habitats are just as valuable. With the redevelopment of the huge Creek mouth sites and the land up and down the banks, the only chance to sustain diversity is for the new developments to include opportunities for wildlife – not plantings but space and privacy for natural colonisation to occur. If this does not happen we will have destroyed the 'treasure' of Deptford Creek.

In addition to the valuable baseline information established by the surveys, this book draws together ideas, opinions, attitudes and debates which have been developed over the three-year process of surveying. It aims to celebrate the unique asset we have inherited, predict and monitor the impacts of change, and influence the process of Creekside renewal.

Having learned lessons none of us will forget, we want to share our experience more widely, in the hope that planners and regenerators throughout the country will find it inspirational and useful. By involving local people in the surveying process and the debates which ensue, the assets of an area can be identified before it is too late. When a recent public meeting in Creekside asked the question "what does regeneration mean to you?" the majority of participants answered "destruction": of communities, of the environment, of the familiarity of our favourite places. We hope that this book will help promote the concept of renewal without destruction.

"Don't it always seem to be
That you don't know what you've got
Till it's gone...
They paved Paradise and put up a parking lot."
– Joni Mitchell

Jess Steele, December 1998

survey zones and wharf names

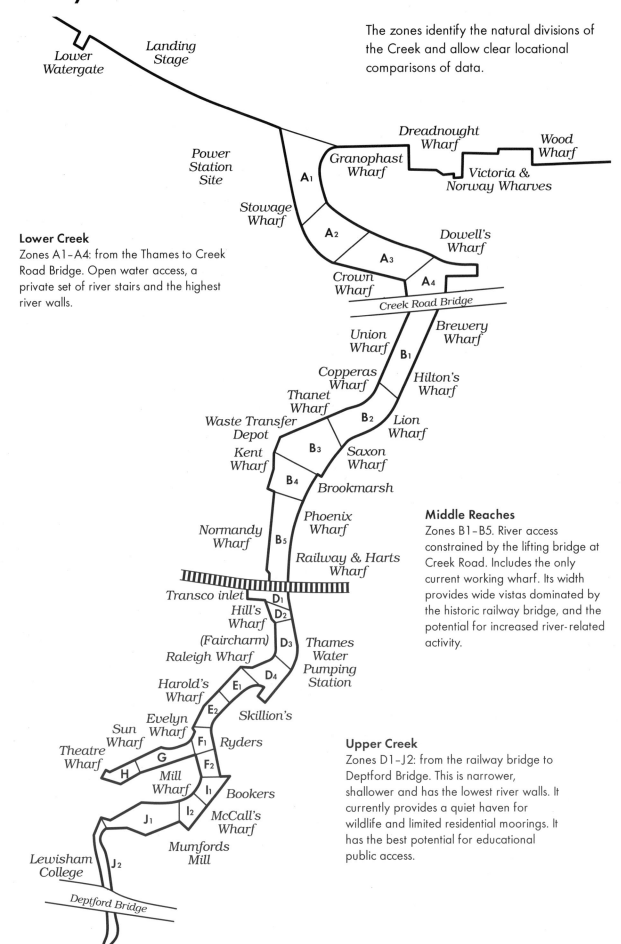

The zones identify the natural divisions of the Creek and allow clear locational comparisons of data.

Lower Creek

Zones A1–A4: from the Thames to Creek Road Bridge. Open water access, a private set of river stairs and the highest river walls.

Middle Reaches

Zones B1–B5. River access constrained by the lifting bridge at Creek Road. Includes the only current working wharf. Its width provides wide vistas dominated by the historic railway bridge, and the potential for increased river-related activity.

Upper Creek

Zones D1–J2: from the railway bridge to Deptford Bridge. This is narrower, shallower and has the lowest river walls. It currently provides a quiet haven for wildlife and limited residential moorings. It has the best potential for educational public access.

Lower Watergate

Landing Stage

Power Station Site

Dreadnought Wharf

Wood Wharf

Granophast Wharf

Victoria & Norway Wharves

A1

Stowage Wharf

A2

Dowell's Wharf

A3

Crown Wharf

A4

Creek Road Bridge

Brewery Wharf

Union Wharf

B1

Hilton's Wharf

Copperas Wharf

Thanet Wharf

B2

Lion Wharf

Waste Transfer Depot

B3

Saxon Wharf

Kent Wharf

B4

Brookmarsh

Phoenix Wharf

Normandy Wharf

B5

Railway & Harts Wharf

Transco inlet

D1

Hill's Wharf

D2

(Faircharm)

D3

Thames Water Pumping Station

Raleigh Wharf

D4

Harold's Wharf

E1

Evelyn Wharf

E2

Skillion's

Sun Wharf

F1

Ryders

Theatre Wharf

G

F2

H

Mill Wharf

I1

Bookers

J1

I2

McCall's Wharf

Mumfords Mill

Lewisham College

J2

Deptford Bridge

river frontages – Environment Agency identification system

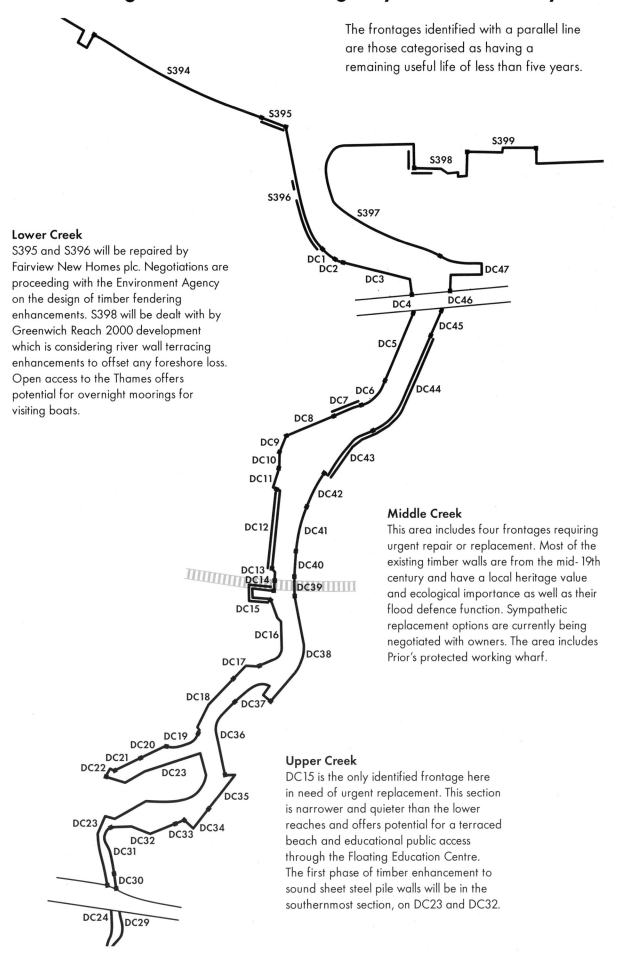

The frontages identified with a parallel line are those categorised as having a remaining useful life of less than five years.

Lower Creek
S395 and S396 will be repaired by Fairview New Homes plc. Negotiations are proceeding with the Environment Agency on the design of timber fendering enhancements. S398 will be dealt with by Greenwich Reach 2000 development which is considering river wall terracing enhancements to offset any foreshore loss. Open access to the Thames offers potential for overnight moorings for visiting boats.

Middle Creek
This area includes four frontages requiring urgent repair or replacement. Most of the existing timber walls are from the mid-19th century and have a local heritage value and ecological importance as well as their flood defence function. Sympathetic replacement options are currently being negotiated with owners. The area includes Prior's protected working wharf.

Upper Creek
DC15 is the only identified frontage here in need of urgent replacement. This section is narrower and quieter than the lower reaches and offers potential for a terraced beach and educational public access through the Floating Education Centre. The first phase of timber enhancement to sound sheet steel pile walls will be in the southernmost section, on DC23 and DC32.

useful addresses

Environment Agency
Thames Regional Office
Kings Meadow House
Kings Meadow Road
Reading RG1 8DQ
Berkshire
0118 953 5000

Port of London Authority
Devon House
58-60 St Katharine's Way
London E1 9LB
0171 265 2656

English Heritage
Fortress House
23 Savile Row
London W1X
0171 973 3000

Royal Commission for the Historical
Monuments of England
55 Blandford Street
London W1H 3AF
0171 208 8200
(RCHME is to be merged with English
Heritage from April 1999)

English Nature - Head Office
Ormond House
26 Boswell Street
London WC1
0171 831 6922

London Ecology Unit
125 Camden High Street
London NW1
0171 267 7944

London Wildlife Trust
Central Office
Harling House
47-51 Great Suffolk Street
London SE1 0BS
0171 261 0447

Creekside Renewal SRB Programme
Creekside Programme Office
60 McMillan Street
London SE8 3HA
0181 312 5503

Planning & Regeneration Team
Leisure, Environment & Economy Directorate
Lewisham Council
Laurence House
1 Catford Road
London SE6 4RU
0181 695 6000

Planning & Regeneration Group
Greenwich Council
Peggy Middleton House
50 Woolwich New Road
London SE18 6HQ
0181 854 8888

Centre for Urban and Community Research
Goldsmiths College
University of London
New Cross
London SE14 6NW
0171 919 7390

Groundwork London
1 Kennington Road
London SE1 7QP
0171 922 1230

Groundwork Vital Centres & Green Links
SRB Programme (Deptford & East
Greenwich)
c/o Deptford Discovery Team
441 New Cross Road
London SE14 6TA
0181 692 7115

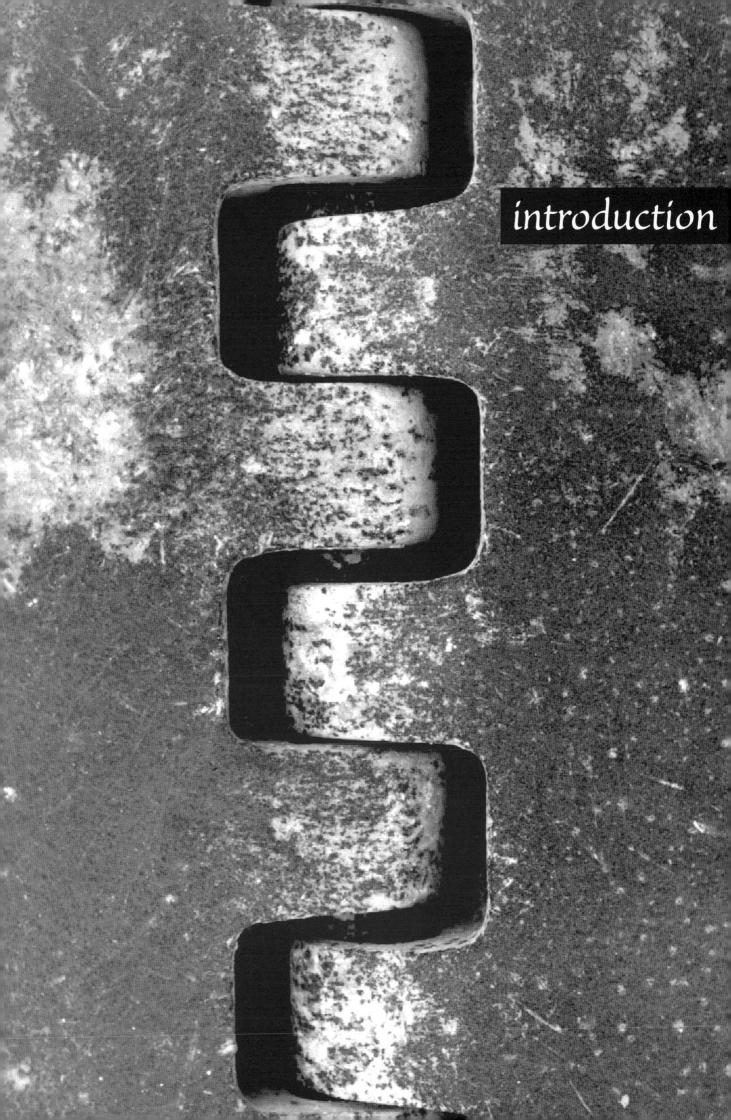

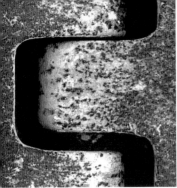

the genius of place

Every place has its 'genius', the distinctive layered textures created over centuries of conflict and co-operation between communities of interest and the landscape they inhabit. Often neglect can be as powerful a force as planned development, allowing nature to create its own regeneration.

This book argues that wastelands are among our most important habitats, more diverse than most 'greenfield' sites, yet it cannot be denied that such spaces are seen to be 'wasted' in terms of human needs. The first dilemma of 'renewal' is weighing up these values in full knowledge of what is there and how it works.

Every development is an opportunity lost; there is no longer the choice of what to create (a hospital, a forest, a school, a theme park). The second dilemma, then, is how to identify needs and build consensus over priorities, while respecting the genius of place.

the ethics of regeneration: first principles

Regeneration is a slippery term. Despite the broad understanding of the causes and consequences of 'urban decay', there is little agreement about what should be done, and how. A decade of intensive publicly-funded 'renewal' in Deptford has left the traces of 18 different regeneration initiatives but a recent report on *The Regeneration Experience* shows that most of the agencies are still failing to learn the lessons of the past. During this period, the language of 'partnership' has become supreme but genuine good practice often takes more time to nurture and create than is envisaged at the bid-writing stage or is feasible within short-term regeneration programmes.

Partnerships take work, time, sensitivity, respect, equality and ongoing resourcing. Regeneration must therefore be sustainable, holistic, participative and rest on knowledge-based decision-making for it to bring a permanent improvement to the local area and economy. You should always assess your assets before you bring in the bulldozers and the bricklayers.

from forgotten parish to strategic location

For some time South East London has been characterised as 'the soft underbelly of the capital', a place of industrial dereliction, cheap sites and demoralised labour. With Michael Heseltine at the Department of the Environment, the old Thameside powerhouse was nicknamed 'the Heselbelt', an exploitable zone in London's strategic development.

This may have looked relatively simple on the map, but the Deptford and Greenwich waterfronts are more complex. The built and social fabric of the area has evolved over centuries as described in the Legacy chapter of this book.

In the early 1990s a number of threads began to emerge which would eventually become the Creekside Renewal Single Regeneration Budget (SRB) programme. With the agreement for the Docklands Light Railway (DLR) Extension, including a commitment of £1m from Deptford City Challenge, Council officers were beginning to discuss 'exit strategies' and the first Creekside Strategy was drafted by the boroughs of Lewisham and Greenwich. The Greenwich Waterfront Development Partnership had been established in 1991 and its Waterfront Strategy was published in 1995. That year the Heritage, Environment & Tourism Group of Deptford Community Forum began a programme of development work to encourage project submissions to City Challenge around Creekside. The Deptford Discovery Team was established to progress a local sustainable transport network, with the Ha'penny Hatch bridge across the Creek at the heart.

The Creekside Strategy, drawn up in 1993 by Lewisham and Greenwich Councils, identified five key objectives to regenerate the area and create a new environment for jobs, housing and community uses
- to create and retain employment opportunities
- to identify and seek greater variety in economic and social activities and opportunities in the Creekside area
- to identify potential uses of the Creek water area
- to identify and improve access possibilities to the Creek and linkages with Greenwich town centre and Deptford High Street
- to identify and secure environmental upgrading opportunities in the area.

It also identified 'Opportunity Areas' of sites available for development in the short term, as part of a mixed land use strategy proposed by the Councils including some office (B1) development combined with housing, retail, recreation and industrial development.

The first Creekside SRB bid contained a variety of projects put forward by the two Councils. Each department was asked to put forward projects – Equalities came up with a sail training project for black women; Education came up with a museum; Planning came up with a north-south footpath along the Ravensbourne. There was nothing wrong with these projects except that they were developed in isolation from the place and people of Creekside. The bid also contained an element of housing renewal which did not fit the aims of Government Office for London at that time. The bid was knocked back at the first stage. However, it had resulted in the formation of the Creekside Implementation Group and a recognition from both Councils that Creekside needed a regenerative programme.

Under some pressure, the Creekside Implementation Group (CIG) gradually expanded to include local people who began to feed in their vision of a renewal programme based on assets rather than problems. The bid began to take on a strong environmental and tourism-related slant. It was renamed 'Building Bridges' in honour of the Ha'penny Hatch bridge, the proposed Creek Mouth bridge, and the less tangible but equally important reforging of links between the historic towns of Deptford and Greenwich.

Few people recognised at the time the intensity of the development pressure the area would face, or the lack of consensus about what constitutes 'renewal without destruction'. Those who did, and who were most concerned about it, tended to be local ecologists whose voices were rarely heeded.

Lewisham Council employed Emma Peters, author of a successful SRB bid in another area, to work up the new bid. Emma recognised the value of local knowledge and worked closely with Jill Goddard who was seconded from the Nature Conservation Team to work full-time in Creekside.

Jill Goddard proposed and developed two projects which we now know were the key to help the Creek survive the regeneration process. Their official titles are Cleaning & Greening the Creek and the Floating Education Centre. Together they have become known as the Creek Environment Project.

Their stated purposes are:
- to protect and enhance the environment of the Creek
- to improve public access and understanding
- to remove rubbish
- to repair identified flood defence risks
- to repair or replace 750 metres of river wall.

renewal surveying in Creekside

Creekside is like a box of treasures which has been left for a thousand years. We should take care, find out what's there, build a consensus about how to treat it. Instead the dynamite of development pressure is blowing the box apart and scattering the dust.

Penny Metal

Jill Goddard and her assistant Jon Ducker

Alongside an unusually strong local knowledge, Jill's strength lay in a wealth of contacts and a willingness to take advice. She understood the importance of "finding out what's already there" and set about planning a series of surveys, in addition to those which would have been carried out anyway. With advice from her contacts, many of them local people with wildlife knowledge, she drew up a series of briefs. "However clear the brief is you have to be flexible. No single person can ever know how to tackle all these different areas professionally. You need a pool of people. I was finding they were ringing up saying "are you sure you are covering my bit?" They will want to advise you, so we had lots of draft briefs whizzing backwards and forwards, which helped. A lot of them were local residents who came to the public meetings and realised there was a way they could contribute.

"Once people had gone out and had a close look, they were coming back saying 'I am working to this brief, but you really need to do a bit more if you are going to start changing the walls', and that led us into another phase. For example the birds survey is still running every year as we originally created it, but we are doing extra work to advise us on exactly what sort of niches in the walls the birds are using, which the bird survey sheet counting method would never do."

The other lesson learnt about surveying was that timing is crucial: the surveys need to be related to each other and timed in relation to their subject rather than the dictates of funding regimes. The bat survey, for example, was undertaken at the wrong time of year. "This was a problem I had in the first year. I had so many surveys to get going that it was like a production line and it was difficult to think about the needs of the individual survey-ors. So inevitably some people were going out in October when they should have been out in midsummer. Tinkering about in the mud in January is not nice for the person doing it!

It takes a lot of work to commission the surveys, and the tendering process slowed it right down. The whole process needs a lot more planning in advance. The first six months of a regeneration programme is ridden with problems which are not really acknowledged. You get the money and off you go, only then you hit even the simple things: where are you going to sit, where is your phone, where is your computer? And that's before you start on the work!"

The surveys included two large-scale 'renewal' surveys – 'Environmental Enhancements' and 'Landscape, Recreation and Access'. These were useful in offering a starting point for discussion, providing maps and displays for public meetings. However, the timetable of the programme created a pressure to find solutions before the baseline survey work had been completed and its lessons absorbed. New proposals for regeneration programmes to have a 'Year Zero' for set up and planning, in which major design work is not expected, is a welcome improvement and is bound to secure better value for money.

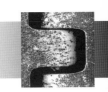

Surveying can be relatively inexpensive, but even in partnership with the Environment Agency, the surveys cost around twice what had been allocated. It was only through an additional contribution from Lewisham Council capital programme that the money was made available. Using local expertise wherever possible has extended the value of this funding enormously. For example, with the cuts in travelling time, delays caused by bad weather can be easily and quickly rescheduled.

"I would like to think that programmes in other areas will be influenced by what we have done and earmark adequate resources to it from the beginning."

survey prices

Many of the surveyors have donated time for free, so these prices should not be seen as transferable to other contexts.

legacy

Dr Chris Phillpotts	desktop survey	£ 2,800
Drs David & Märit Gaimster	reassessment of Broadway finds,	£ 3,000
MoLAS	foreshore	£ 3,000
Mike Canty	rubbish	£ 1,850

life of the Creek

University of Greenwich	mud and water	£10,000
Natural History Museum	algae	£ 2,400
Conservation Works	flora	£ 2,000 +
	(2nd stage)	£ 4,950
Unicomarine	aquatic invertebrates*	£11,000
Physalia Ltd	aquatic invertebrates	£ 1,475
Richard A. Jones	terrestrial invertebrates	£ 7,600
Environment Agency	fish*	£ 3,000
Dusty Gedge	birds (1998+9)	£ 1,800 +
		£ 2,500
Mike Paice	birds	£ 150
London Ecology Unit	birds	£ 1,680
Clive Herbert	bats	£ 595
Deptford Discovery Team	human users	£ 500

renewal

W.S. Atkins	barrage	£ 6,000
Babtie Group	flood defence*	£50,000
Robert West Consulting	themes/environmental enhancements	£20,000
Urban Initiatives	land use, access and recreation	£20,000

* commissioned by the Environment Agency

One of the clearest conclusions from the survey process is that, despite its value, it is two years too late. "Regeneration policy should take this into account. You should be able to apply for, say, £100,000 which you have to match, to do surveying (whether that's about wildlife or housing conditions or deprivation. You do that first and then you go back to Government Office and say 'what we need is XYZ'. This publication would then be part of the bid and we would know exactly what needed to be done, whereas in the meantime there has been a lot of development pressure and a lot of public money spent on projects which are not necessarily reflecting the priorities. The whole idea of the surveys is to find out what you've got before you ruin it, yet here some of the ruin is already cutting in and we're not getting a pre-programme baseline. I think it's inevitable that you're always going to be running behind some disaster but the idea of the surveys is to prevent some future disasters."

If the ultimate point of pre-renewal surveying is damage limitation, there are also a number of other benefits. "When I started off I just thought we need to know what's there but now I've realised that the surveys are helping us design what we are going to do. And also, with planning applications coming in thick and fast, the surveys are giving us an informed view to make comments and to help developers change their designs in a way that will add to the overall sustainable improvement of the area."

The surveyors are experts in their fields. Many of them are also local residents. The diversity and value of local skills should be recognised in tender lists including local candidates wherever possible. "The surveys are actually giving jobs to local people, jobs in fields they care about a great deal. Here we are moving towards a kind of Local Labour in Consultancy, rather than construction and cleaning and catering and all the things that we usually get offered, we are getting a level of work which matches the skills of local people. You get more from local people - they are available at times of the day which you'd have to pay exorbitant amounts to get from anyone else, they keep an eye out for anything which might affect the flora or the birds or whatever, and they stay around so they keep on monitoring long after the contract is over."

The Creek Environment Project has established a scheme for consultancies under £500 (the highest threshold for a contract to be awarded to a single contractor, assuming that value for money has been established). This has spread the established network by advertising in a local paper, in shop windows, libraries and community halls and having a simple form for people to express what they can offer and a price on their time. Above the £500 threshold people can apply for inclusion on Greenwich Council's Approved List of Contractors. It is an opportunity for local people to be involved and to have their contribution properly valued.

Another asset acquired by the project was a room in Drake House, a building owned by Lewisham Council. Known as 'the Den', this was a space for the surveyors and other advisers to meet and work alone and in small groups. The walls are covered with maps, photographs and sketches, and copies of the survey reports are available there. "It seemed that you could sit in a room in Catford or Woolwich and talk about Creekside but most of the people wouldn't know where we were talking about. I think photographs of the area would help kick people's minds into gear about some of the issues they are worried about."

an ecology meeting at the Den

Jill Goddard

exploring the Creek at low tide

'My first reaction to Creekside is that it's a fascinating area. I don't live here, but somehow I seem to have a great affinity with it. I know a lot of people who do live here and I've worked on nature reserve sites here. But you only have to look at it to feel that. I worry that other people don't go out and look at the site that you are talking about. When they look at it they're astounded that the Cutty Sark is just down the road and the history doesn't stop next to the Cutty Sark, it goes on, and when you start reading about the background, it just bowls you over. The more you learn about Deptford and the Creek, the more it fascinates you. It's not just what you're looking at, the dereliction and the rubbish, its all that's gone before, all that's tucked behind the wall, all that's underneath the buildings that are there now. Look at what they found on the Power Station site. That just confirmed everything that I ever felt – there it all was uncovered. The old wall next to the sea wall, wonderful! I found it magical. So there is that side of it which is very personal and then on the work side it's wonderful that the environmental element is a major part of this regeneration programme. Not just an add on, not just a small project, but almost what the rest of the programme hinges on, because if we don't do something with the Creek, the area will never change. But it's a real challenge to make sure that we hang on to some good practice and not just end up with anything that looks pretty.

"I find the challenge is that you get very opposing views on what we should be doing, but when you get people down for maybe an hour and you can explain why something is good the way it is, a whole new vista seems to open up and people never cease to astound me how they will appreciate a slightly different way of repairing the river wall, once they are given a chance to understand why. To some extent it's not about changing what we are looking at, but changing the way we are looking at it, which is why the education and visitor centre is so important. There may not be rose beds but... "

making the decisions

What happens in the Creek is directly related to what happens on the land, so the Creek Environment Project's interest in 'renewal' is broader than environmental protection. The project was developed with the basic principles of partnership at its core and genuine partnership results in the evolution of networks which actually change the direction of work while still adhering to the agreed objectives of the project. If community involvement means anything it must be able to influence how and what is delivered with public money. "I think it is very hard because bidding rounds always seem to follow one after the other very fast, but more resources need to be put into each bid. Government Office for London used to expect everything to happen in the early stages but now they are recognising that people should be given a chance to find their feet and set up those communication links so that the projects have a degree of flexibility when you finally start spending big money, you know you are doing it right."

One of the earliest partnerships was established with the Groundwork *Vital Centres & Green Links* SRB, a parallel but much smaller local environmental regeneration initiative. When Groundwork chose the Deptford Discovery Team (leaders of the Ha'penny Hatch project within the Creekside SRB) as its local programme managers, the connections were multiplied.

Both SRB programmes began in April 1996. Groundwork and the Creek Environment Project hosted a public meeting that month to bring together environmental interests in the

area and reach out to the vast majority of local residents who were not yet aware of the programmes. The meeting was very successful, both in numbers and in the warmth and enthusiasm of contributions. The Creekside Environment Open Meetings have been held every six weeks ever since. Minutes are sent to a mailing list of over 330 people, including councillors and officers, riparian owners, statutory authorities, and many local individuals, groups and tenants associations. To avoid spending all the time on report-backs, a written update is provided on current or proposed projects, giving the opportunity for detailed discussions about issues such as river walls, rubbish, habitat creation, or specific projects.

The meetings are often heated but almost always humourous. Perhaps unfortunately, councillors, officers and regeneration agency staff have rarely attended and it has become clear that more understanding of the role and methods of community consultation is necessary. Recognising consultation initiatives as an 'output' might help. Community partnership is about equality of status, about valuing and using the contribution of diverse expertise. Heated discussion usually means that people care. Since ongoing partnership breeds familiarity, mutual understanding and respect and a continued interest in working together, it can sometimes appear nepotistic or cliquey, yet the network here in Creekside has proved remarkably open and inclusive.

So far, community expertise has saved the environmental programme a great deal of money by helping it to direct its resources in the most practical direction at any one time and keeping its overall objectives linked to all the developments happening in the same area. The open meetings are also performing an enabling role in helping local residents see how they can independently contribute to regeneration programmes, allowing them to put forward complementary projects for Community Chest or contingency funding. This is expanding the beneficial impact of regeneration funding on the area.

"Communication and consultation are my messages, and real involvement of people. All these changes are for the benefit of the local community and there is concern to be sure it really benefits the local community. I think that all of us, myself included, have to be constantly checking that we are doing that, all the way through. Through consulting and communicating and involving people, people will help you check that."

To help build consensus around the detail of the proposed environmental enhance-ments, a smaller group of surveyors and advisers has been meeting six-weekly since 1997. Known as the ecology meetings although it debates a wide range of issues relevant to the whole ecosystem of Deptford Creek, this group has become a 'think-tank' which discusses developments and proposals as they arise and pools its knowledge to create detailed briefs for the enhancement work. It is expected to continue to meet to assist with monitoring and management of the Creek.

Consultation and information for the wider community has been helped by Jill Goddard's attendance at Deptford Community Forum and the recently constituted Creekside Forum meetings. The Creek Environment Project has produced a general leaflet/poster about the Creek and a leaflet about the black redstart. We hope that this publication will also serve to inform local people in detail about the Creek's historic legacy, its current wildlife and about enhancement proposals.

legacy

valuing our inheritance

Creekside is a special place, literally moulded by centuries of human interaction with a very particular landscape. It would be hard to find another place with so much history so undervalued and neglected.

The Creek was the reason for settlement and continued to be the key to development, both a great incentive and a major headache. The struggle to contain the water, defend the settlements against flooding and drain the marshland went alongside the intensive use of both Creek and Thames for fishing, transport, milling, shipbuilding and, later, to supply and run the world's first power station.

The importance of the history of Creekside is not only that it tells us how we got where we are and explains the legacy we inherit, but also that it can inform and inspire decision-making for the future. There are multiple threads in the history of Creekside and all of them remain relevant today – flood defence, shipbuilding and boating, industrial uses and pollution, the international communities of wildlife, the acute poverty and the attempts to overcome its effects.

Archaeology – *the buried heritage* – is "a fragile and finite resource". Legislation, policy and guidance exists to protect and value our heritage, primarily in the form of Planning Policy Guidance PPG15 Planning & the Historic Environment and PPG16 Archaeology & Planning. English Heritage are currently working with other organisations to generate debate on sustaining the historic environment and some pointers from their initial discussion document are included here. More local guidance is to be found in the Unitary Development Plans (UDPs) of Greenwich and Lewisham Councils. Both authorities began reviewing their UDPs in 1998 and expect to complete in 2001. The decisions made at this stage will have a radical effect on the future survival of the Creekside legacy.

The story of Creekside from prehistoric times to the present is a tale of both people and landscapes. In this section we explore the legacy of Creekside through a number of surveys, including research into the Creek channel and its containing walls, the foreshore and the rubbish, as well as the story of human life in Creekside.

Penny Metal

why survey the legacy?

Local history and archaeological remains are important assets which can assist in regeneration through urban design, education and local amenity. Furthermore, the local planning authorities have a statutory responsibility to conserve historic remains and are expected to follow government guidance which establishes procedures for informed decision-making.

The archaeological surveys – both desktop and foreshore – were designed to assess the character, quality and extent of archaeological structures and deposits within the area, raise local awareness and determine the general impact that any development might have on the archaeological resource.

The foreshore survey forms a basic starting point by accurately locating and characterising features of the Creek, while the desktop survey provides a broader historical context for development strategy.

Both enable detailed and accurate advice on the likely scope of development impact and allow for mitigation strategies to be prepared in advance. Substantial changes to the walls, bed and hinterland of the Creek during redevelopment may significantly affect deposits and structures potentially covering the last 5,000 years. Proposed developments and infrastructure schemes elsewhere in the area will require detailed individual archaeological desk-based assessments followed by field evaluations to help devise mitigation strategies combining preservation and excavation. Conservation will be best served by a design approach which is sensitive to the presence of the archaeological resource and sufficiently flexible to allow for the preservation in situ of selected elements.

The basic findings of the surveys will remain current for a long time and will aid planners, architects, engineers and historians. In combination with other surveys they can be used to plan educational activities and visitor attractions in the field. The aim is to present the historic environment with its many metaphors regarding stability and change, so that the local community recognise and value these 'remains' as a shared cultural asset, offering opportunities for personal exploration of Creekside's distinct sense of place and character.

mouth of Deptford Creek, 1810. From 'Old and New London'

surveys and research

There are numerous ways of surveying the 'legacy' of an area like Creekside, varying in geographical scope, research techniques and methods of analysing and presenting the findings. With the help of local historians, archaeological advisors and practitioners, a combination of approaches has been used in Creekside to sketch the historical outline and to promote understanding of the importance of the surviving assets.

In 1884 **Nathan Dews** published his *History of Deptford,* very much in the style of the time, full of lists of local worthies, ships built and launched, and some rather dubious but entertaining stories. As he wrote in his introduction, "I must frankly confess that had I known the labour the work would entail in research and preparation when it was first suggested to me, I fear I should not have commenced with so light a heart as I did."

After more than a century of neglect, Deptford's "special and spectacular 2000 year history" was presented by Jess Steele in *Turning the Tide: The History of Everyday Deptford* published by **Deptford Forum Publishing** in November 1993. A wide-ranging book with the explicit aim of encouraging local pride and understanding of both past and present, *Turning the Tide* is now out of print having sold 3,000 copies.

Despite Creekside's proximity to Greenwich it has not featured highly in the local histories which tend to focus on Royal Greenwich. However, a useful study has been undertaken of the former barge repair site at Wood Wharf by **Stephen Jones** on behalf of Groundwork.

In 1994 **Pre-Construct Archaeology** completed a detailed desktop study of the Greenwich Reach site at the mouth of the Creek. Pre-Construct continued their work in the area, first with a desktop study considering the St Paul's Rectory (1995) as part of the Deptford City Challenge St Paul's Initiative and later with a study of Lower Watergate (1996) for the Deptford Community Boatyard project.

The Creek Environment Project surveys, conducted during the first half of 1997, were
- a desktop study by **Dr Chris Phillpotts** on the wider Creekside area
- a foreshore survey by the **Museum of London Archaeological Service (MoLAS)**
- a reassessment of the Deptford Broadway finds by **Dr David & Dr Märit Gaimster**

In the meantime, the area's most important historic site was being dug up for the Fairview New Homes development. Pre-Construct Archaeology undertook the excavation, focusing on two areas, the first next to St Nicholas' churchyard and the other on the site of the East India Company yard.

The **Royal Commission for Historic Monuments** have recently undertaken an historic buildings survey of Deptford High Street and Tanners Hill, where they found important evidence of early vernacular architecture connected to the domestic buildings of the American seaboard as well as some "rare witnesses of...Georgian London".

The legacy of Creekside is made of mud and rubbish as well as buildings and stories. Two further surveys commissioned by the Environment Project are relevant both to the legacy and to renewal:
- rubbish by **Mike Canty**
- baseline chemical survey of the sediments and waters of Deptford Creek by the **University of Greenwich** (see Renewal: Mud & Water).

techniques

In defining and creating briefs for the archaeological surveys the Creek Environment Project was assisted by the **Greater London Archaeological Advisory Service (GLAAS)** of English Heritage. Ken Whittaker of GLAAS maintained involvement throughout the surveying and the preparation of this publication.

desktop survey

Single surveyor: archaeological consultant, Dr Chris Phillpotts

- consultation and analysis of the Greater London Sites & Monuments Record (GLSMR) in a 3km radial zone centred on the study area
- analysis of published and unpublished reports of previous archaeological investigations in and around the study area
- information extracted from printed and manuscript maps of the area from 17th to 20th centuries and plotted to scale on reconstruction maps
- information extracted from secondary and primary printed sources and also from manuscript sources
- analysis of the records of geotechnical surveys ('boreholes') to create surface models and reconstruction maps
- site visits and photographic record of the whole study area
- liaison with the MoLAS survey of the Creek bed walls
- consultation with the other historians and archaeologists working in the Deptford area.

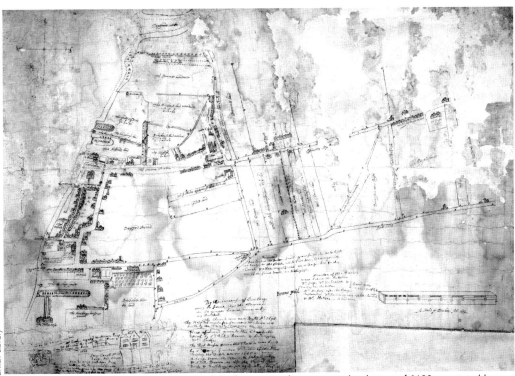

British Library

'The Evelyn Map'. First authentic publication of this fascinating document, a sketch map of 1623 annotated by John Evelyn some time after 1652. The map has been 'tidied up' many times by other historians but the tears and gaps mirror the inevitable missing bits in our historical understanding.

foreshore survey

Survey Team: Field archaeologist, two archaeological surveyors, an archaeological photographer and a geomatics specialist, Museum of London Archaeological Service.

- intensive survey involving identification of foreshore and Creek-bed features
- feature and contour plotting using Total Station theodolite, Ordnance Survey control, PenMap surveying software
- photographic survey of selected features
- comparison of surveyed features to borehole data survey
- health and safety issues, including protective clothing (ie. full-length waders); necessary care taken in areas of quicksand; taking a careful note of tidal position; and being aware of potential dangers – a World War II shell was discovered and removed from the Creek foreshore prior to the main survey.

Metropolitan Police Service (River Thames division) with the World War II shell

reassessment of finds

Survey Team: 2 professional archaeologists, Drs David & Märit Gaimster

- systematic survey of the Deptford Broadway collection held in Lewisham Local Studies Library
- quantitative analysis of all finds and assessment of conservation needs
- evaluation of priority conservation needs especially Anglo-Saxon grave finds
- comparative analysis of local archaeological finds and material within Greater London
- a photographic record of selected material.

Roman greyware flagon which had been stuck together with parcel tape

excavation at Greenwich Reach

Survey Team: Two supervisors, two assistant supervisors, twenty field archaeologists, a finds supervisor and two finds assistants. Specialist advice was taken from several visiting consultants. The field team was supported by a project management team.

- the site was evaluated, areas of surviving archaeology identified and research objectives established
- the general overburden was machine excavated
- the archaeological deposits, features and structures were systematically excavated and recorded
- the stratified finds and samples were retrieved during the excavation for post-excavation study
- the results of the excavation were assessed, and revised research objectives established for analysis and publication

excavation techniques at Greenwich Reach

little fish films

- after assessment, the finds will be stored at the Museum of London
- standard Health and Safety procedures for construction sites were followed, ie. the Construction (Design and Management) Regulation 1994 and Management of Health and Safety at Work Regulation 1992.

historic buildings survey

Survey Team: Historian, photographer and graphics officer from the Royal Commission's London Emergency Recording Section with specialist help from the University of Delaware.

- field survey of houses along with documentary research from archives
- photography of interior and exterior of houses
- illustrating and writing of report

Royal Commission on the Historical Monuments of England

number 150 (right) is probably the oldest building in Deptford High Street

Creekside story

There are three main threads in the Creekside story
- a shifting of settlement focus between the three key locations (Broadway, Deptford Green, Deptford Strand)
- attempts to control the Thames and Creek to protect the land from flooding
- the development of industry, including the shipyards and the Power Station, and their subsequent decline.

the prehistoric landscape

The story begins in palaeolithic times, around 430,000 years ago. This period lasted until 8500BC and so represents more than 98% of all 'history'. This was a time of massive geological and climate changes and the present course of the Thames was only established at the end of the period. The Thames originally flowed to the North Sea through the Vale of St Albans and across East Anglia. It was diverted into its present valley when the Vale of St Albans was blocked by the advancing ice sheet.

tides

Throughout the historical record the theme of Deptford Creek runs strong. In the times when it was known as the Rondesbourne or Rantesbourne it was clearly a dynamic and dangerous river, always flooding, shoaling and shifting its course. In the constant struggle to confine and control it, the ever-rising level of the high tides was the critical determinant of settlement and land use along its banks which rose in a series of chronological steps. In the management of the river walls and tidemill floodgates, a few inches made a crucial difference.

creek walls

It is not known exactly when the lower Thames was embanked but it may have been as early as the Saxon period. The early river walls consisted of simple earthen banks, perhaps founded on hurdles. By the 16th century timber groynes probably formed the foundation and the earth may have been mixed with reeds from the marshes in front of the wall. Almost the whole length of the Creek was still lined with earthen embankments in the 1770s. Over the centuries each time a wall has been replaced the new wall has been built a little further into the river itself. This encroachment means that archaeologists can find remains of the older walls many metres behind the present-day wall.

centuries of river walls

Pre-Construct Archaeology

Throughout the Ice Ages the Thames and its tributaries retreated in stages, leaving the old flood-plains behind as gravel terraces. Alluvium clays were deposited by flooding and during regular periods of *transgression* (when the sea level rises). These are interspersed with bands of peat, deposited during periods of *regression* (when the sea level falls).

Some of the peat layers have been deposited by previous channels of the Ravensbourne. They show that the Creek was generally broader, had a wide delta at its meeting with the Thames, and ran in a straighter course from south to north (see p20-21 – maps). One notable former channel of the Creek lies under Union Wharf and Crown Wharf to the west of Creek Road bridge.

Within the prehistoric flood plain of the Thames, gravel islands stood proud above the level of the surrounding marshes. One such island existed at the Ida Works in Grinstead Road, another may have lain on the east side of the Creek mouth.

Palaeolithic people left flint tools in Deptford and Rotherhithe and animal bones show that there were mammoths, woolly rhinoceros and reindeer roaming the Thames valley during the last glacial stage of the period.

Mesolithic people (8500-4000BC) probably lived along the edges of the gravel terraces, using the marshy land below for hunting, fishing and gathering. The Thames foreshore is the most promising for mesolithic finds and a grey flint axe was found near Pepys Estate in 1984.

Neolithic artefacts (4000-2000BC) include an axe at Norway Wharf and one at Deptford Strand which had come originally from Cornwall, showing the trade routes for axes of this period.

Elsewhere in the Thames flood-plain excavations have found **Bronze Age** (2000-700BC) wooden trackways. The marshy delta at the mouth of the Ravensbourne could have been used for grazing, fishing and fowling, connected to the terrace edge settlements with similar causeways. The promontory of St Nicholas provided a dry route to the delta marsh in the medieval period and may have been used in this way much earlier.

Evidence of **Iron Age** (700BC-100AD) settlement is poor but finds at the Dover Castle site on Deptford Broadway, and comparisons with sites at Woolwich, Charlton and other river cliff locations, make Iron Age occupation likely at the Broadway and possible at the Creek mouth.

The confluence of the Wandle and the Thames, a comparable location, was a favoured place for making votive offerings. Expensive and ornate objects were placed in the river waters. Evidence from several periods may therefore be buried beneath the alluvium around the Creek mouth and the peat-filled former channels of the Creek must be seen as potential find-spots for ritually deposited artefacts, and also ancient boats.

romans

The Roman conquest of the first century AD brought new patterns to the local landscape. One of the great debates of local history is the path of the Roman road from Dover to Londinium, later called Watling Street. It ran a straight course through Bexleyheath, Welling and Shooters Hill to Greenwich Park, apparently aligned to a river crossing at Westminster. From Greenwich its course is unclear.

If the straight course continued it would have crossed the Park area diagonally down a steep hill to cross the Ravensbourne near the mouth of Deptford Creek. The water level at the Creek mouth was four metres lower in the Roman period than now. Portions of gravel road metalling which may have been parts of the Roman road were found in Greenwich Park. When Humphrey, Duke of Gloucester, enclosed the Park in 1434 he was given royal license to close a road which may have been a Roman remnant. A possible trace of this road, a low escarpment running east–west, has been recorded in the south east part of the park.

Most writers believe it is more probable that Watling Street deviated to the south of Greenwich to avoid the marshy lands around the Creek mouth, crossing the Ravensbourne close to where Deptford Bridge now stands and continuing along the line of Deptford Broadway, New Cross Road and the Old Kent Road. It is not known if the Ravensbourne was crossed by a bridge or a ford at either point.

A Roman settlement was established at the Broadway. In 1866 substantial Roman brick foundations along with a tessellated pavement were revealed at the junction with Deptford High Street. Other finds have included a blackware urn of burnt human bones discovered at the Kent Waterworks in Brookmill Road in 1853. Excavations on the site of the Dover Castle in 1989 and 1992 revealed the boundary ditches and rubbish pits of a settlement dating from the 2nd to the 4th century AD. One pit contained a wide range of ceramics mainly from the Greater London area. The end of the Roman occupation is represented by a Nene Valley colour-coated bottle of the late 4th century. Trade with the Continent is reflected in the fragments of jugs and flagons imported from North East Gaul.

Comparisons with other locations suggest there may have been a Roman river port in the area. This could have been at the mouth of the Creek where Roman coins, pottery and tile have been found.

deptford broadway settlement

In 1992 a small-scale excavation behind the Dover Castle public house on the north side of the Broadway, produced the first archaeological evidence of Anglo-Saxon settlement at Deptford. Here two inhumation burials were recovered, some 6m apart and both on a north east – south west alignment. In the southernmost grave were found surviving parts of the legs and left arm of an adult. Traces of a wooden coffin could be identified in an outline of dark soil, supported by a series of iron coffin nails appearing on two levels in the grave fill. No finds were associated with the skeleton, but the grave fill also produced three pieces of coarse, hand-made pottery.

The second grave contained the remains of an adult woman, furnished with a rich selection of grave-goods dating to the 7th century. The finds included a necklace of 11 glass beads, a gold-wire ring and a gilt-bronze pendant cast with animal-style interlace ornament, set with a small garnet on gold-foil in the centre. The pendant was originally a mount for a bronze cauldron, re-used as an amulet. Its ornament is related to a group of embossed gold pendants found in South East England. Close to the woman's right knee was a copper-alloy bracelet of twisted wire, and on her left leg was a small bronze buckle that probably belonged to a garter-strap. In the area around the feet were iron fittings for a wooden casket, together with bits of Roman glass and a shale spindle-whorl, which may have been stored in the casket. A further spindle-whorl was found nearby, just outside the grave fill.

The Broadway burials are important, not only for Deptford, but also for our knowledge of the wider London area in the Middle Saxon period. Contemporary with the barrows in Greenwich Park, as well as burials known from the grounds of the National Maritime Museum, the Broadway graves indicate that both sides of the river Ravensbourne were settled at this time.

saxons

Until recently, the series of barrows in Greenwich Park, thought to be from the 7th century, was one of few known sites of Anglo-Saxon activity in London south of the Thames. So the discovery of two parallel graves at Deptford Broadway in 1992 is very important. They are likely to be part of an as yet uninvestigated Middle Saxon cemetery.

The name Deptford, 'the deep ford', is thought to be Anglo-Saxon in origin, referring to the crossing at the Ravensbourne of the Old Roman Road. In medieval documentary sources, however, the present area of Deptford is referred to as the manor of West Greenwich. From the Domesday Book, William the Conqueror's land survey of 1086, we know that before the Norman Conquest *Greenviz* was held as two manors: one by Earl Harold Godwinson, the other by one Brixi Cild. It has been suggested that this division corresponds to the two settlement centres at the Broadway and at Deptford Strand.

Both Deptford and Greenwich were part of the Lewisham multiple estate in the late Saxon period. Such estates allowed different agricultural and pastoral functions to be spread over a wide area, taking advantage of the local variation such as upland and lowland zones of arable, pasture, woodland and marshland.

Staff at the British Museum Department of Medieval and Later Antiquities have stressed the regional and national importance of the collection. Their colleagues in the Conservation Department have identified an urgent need for conservation treatment.

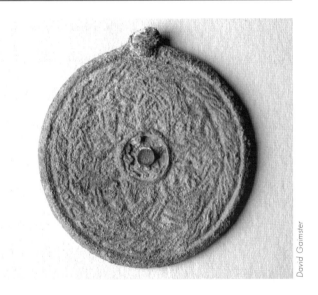
David Gaimster

Various local groups, including the Lewisham Local History Society, have added their concerns about the care of the artefacts.

English Heritage has now asked the London borough of Lewisham to submit an application for a small grant to support the cost of conservation work. It is hoped that this will secure the immediate future of the artefacts, particularly the pendant, and allow further consideration of their long-term care and display.

David Gaimster

finds from the Anglo-Saxon graves at Deptford Broadway

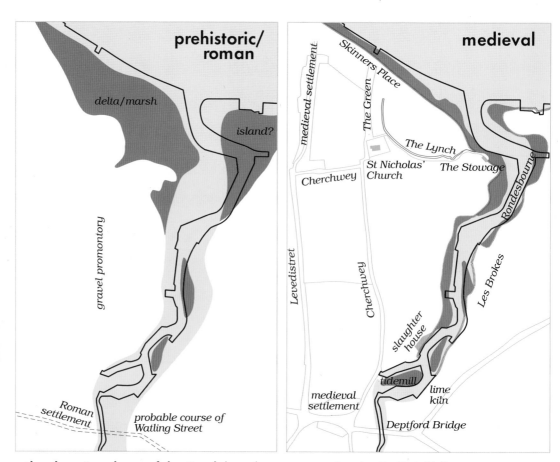

prehistoric/roman

delta/marsh

island?

gravel promontory

Roman settlement

probable course of Watling Street

medieval

medieval settlement

Skinners Place

The Green

The Lynch

St Nicholas' Church

The Stowage

Cherchwey

Rondesbourne

Levedistret

Cherchwey

Les Brokes

slaughter house

tidemill

lime kiln

medieval settlement

Deptford Bridge

the changing shape of the Creek based on reconstructions by Dr Chris Phillpotts
the modern Creek, shown on maps as a black outline, is the result of centuries of encroachment

It is not known when the parish church of St Nicholas was founded. The site would have been dramatic in the Saxon period, "a low gravel cliff overlooking seasonally flooded marshes towards the Thames. When flood waters rose it would have been almost on an island" (Phillpotts). Historians suggest it was a daughter-church of St Alfege's at Greenwich, which was founded after the

oldest known view of St Nicholas' Church and Trinity almshouses

martyrdom of Alfege, archbishop of Canterbury, on the site in 1012. The earliest references to St Nicholas are in the Textus Roffensis of circa 1115 and when the right to appoint the rector was granted to Bayham Abbey around 1183.

medieval Creekside

In the Domesday survey of 1086 neither the present Deptford nor Greenwich were mentioned by those names. The bulk of Greenwich was included in the large estate of Levesham, while Deptford was referred to as the manor of Greenviz (ie West Greenwich), held by Gilbert de Maminot from Bishop Odo of Bayeux, the brother of William the Conqueror. Apart from a brief time when the manor was held by the Templars, it remained in the Maminot family until the late 12th century when it passed to their descendants the de Says. The family became "mighty among the barons of their day and generation" giving the name Say's Court to their Deptford home. Writing in 1884, Dews commented that "the name is preserved despite the vast changes and alterations Deptford has undergone." Even today, after many more changes, part of the site is still known as Sayes Court Gardens.

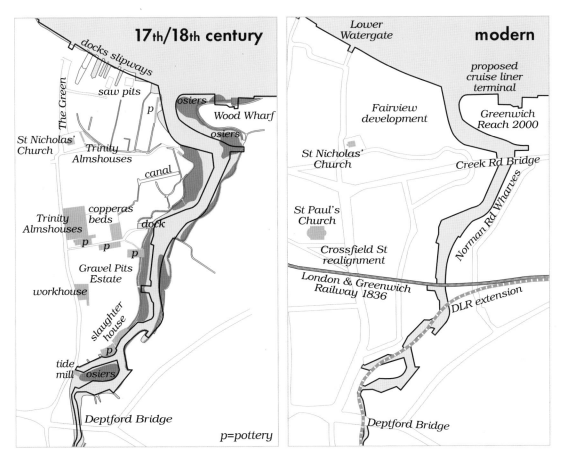

the pale colour shows the Creek channel at different periods, with the mud banks and drainage outlets represented in a darker colour

The fundamental medieval theme was the struggle to reclaim or *inn* the marshes from the river. Earth banks were built and the land behind drained by ditches. In the 14th century local people were appointed as *walreves* to watch over the river walls and royal commissions were established to ensure that repairs were carried out. Nevertheless 60 acres of the Greenwich–Deptford waterfront was lost to the Thames during the 14th century and the river continued to rise. Sometimes breaches in the banks led to new features like the pond of 1293 which was later adapted for the basin in the royal dockyard. One way of stabilising the marshy banks was to plant osiers or willow reeds. The wardens of the Bridge House Estates, who owned substantial lands in Creekside, planted osiers on their lands in the early 15th century.

The main road layout was established by the medieval period, although the names were different. Levidistret was the royal way to Deptford Strand while Churchwey linked the Tide Mill to St Nicholas' Church. These two – now the key roads of Deptford High Street and Deptford Church Street – were linked by a path, also called Churchwey, along the line of McMillan Street. East of the church a path led to the Stowage, a house in existence by at least 1397. The historical map clearly shows the distinctive pattern of Creekside, already laid down in the medieval period.

The settlement at the Broadway was known as Depeford vill and was a focus of dense and continuous occupation. A wooden bridge crossed the Creek from the 1230s and the village grew rapidly between 1230 and 1439 to include shops and inns. The Broadway excavations produced ceramic evidence for continuous settlement from the 10th century. There were wooden wharves beside Deptford Bridge on the east bank and in 1381 a cargo of 4,000 faggots was delivered there for the bread ovens of the village. At the east end of the Bridge there was a hermitage or chapel dedicated to St Katherine, which closed in 1548.

The late Saxon settlement close to St Nicholas' Church had been an outlet for river trade for the large multiple estate of Lewisham but the construction of Gilbert de Magminot's castle may have led to a shift of settlement to the Deptford Strand area. This settlement, called the vill of Westgrenewich or the Stronde, was certainly populated by 1227 when Walter the archer and his wife Christiana were found murdered at their house in West grenewic. The gardens of houses stretched towards the river and wharves were established at the end of some of them by the 1380s.

There is no sign of houses near the church in the 13th century and Dr Phillpotts believes that Deptford Green did not exist at this time, or indeed as late as 1416. Rather it was a part of a late medieval attempt to repopulate the area – an early example of regeneration planning. This may have been connected with work on the fabric of the church, including the steeple and the great bell. The building of the original almshouses by the guild which became Trinity House may also be relevant to this revival.

Deptford Green, circa 1900

early industry and economy

The earliest industry which made use of the Creek itself was the Tide Mill which dates back at least to the 12th century when Walkelin de Maminot granted an annual rent of 10 shillings from the mill to Bermondsey Abbey. Acquired by Christ's Hospital in 1576, the mill's operation caused continual problems of flooding because the millers kept raising the height of the flood-gates by a critical few inches. The mill was destroyed by floods in 1824 and

the tidemill, 1840

rebuilt by J H Robinson who turned it into a steam-powered flour mill. The flood-gates were still causing trouble in the 1850s when they were described as "miserably deficient". Later the mill buildings expanded towards Deptford Bridge and covered the former osier ground on the Lewisham College site. The mill closed in the 1960s and was demolished after a fire in 1970. To its east Mumford's Mill was founded in 1790. The present grade II listed building dates from 1897.

waterworks engineers inspecting 18th century pipes

Nearby was the water mill known as Brook Mill, mentioned in deeds of 1588 and purchased by John Evelyn in 1668. In 1701 two local citizens, William Yarnold and Robert Watson, were given a 500-year charter to raise water from the Ravensbourne and pipe it to the manors of Sayes Court and East Greenwich. This was the beginning of the Ravensbourne Waterworks which survived precariously throughout the 19th century as the Kent Waterworks Company, absorbing local companies throughout North Kent until the formation of the Metropolitan Water Board in 1903. There was also a windmill on the Skillion's site until the 1840s.

There was tile and brickmaking in the area from 1418 and Deptford supplied nearly two million bricks to Henry VIII for his new manor house at Dartford. There was a limekiln in Lez Brokes on the Greenwich banks by 1481. Other industries included gravel digging for boat ballast, a plethora of industrial potteries producing the Deptford ware, tanneries, clay pipe factories and the manufacture of dyes and chemical at the innovative Copperas Works. These were established by Sir Nicholas Crispe in the mid-17th century. The works remained in the family until the 1750s and this may have inspired the name Crispin and Crispiana for the pub where the 'mayor of Deptford' went after Lord Mayor's Day!

Greenwich Palace exerted an increasing influence on Deptford's economy in the 15th and early 16th centuries. Deptford pastured and slaughtered the royal cattle at the slaughterhouse on the site of Harold's Wharf. The Browne family of Sayes Court grazed royal cattle on their fields and supervised the royal slaughterhouses in their role as Clerks of the Green Cloth.

A large part of Deptford remained open pastoral land or was used for market gardening to serve the city of London from the 16th to the 19th centuries. Orchards and market gardens spread rapidly after 1590, with manure brought by barge. There were still market gardens in Broomfield and the Norman Road area in the 1840s and those near the Kent Waterworks survived until the 1880s.

navy building town

On the waterfront the initial basis of the economy was fishing and there are references to fishing at the Strand from 1279. Deptford's most famous industry, shipbuilding, had begun by 1420 and was well established by the end of the 15th century. Tracing the rise and fall of the various local naval institutions can be both confusing and rewarding.

In 1513 Henry VIII established the first **Naval Dockyard** at Deptford. From its foundation growth was so rapid that in less than 40 years the King's Yard at Deptford became the chief Thames dockyard. Royal dockyards, even in peace-time, were the most considerable industrial units in the country. The dockyard brought prosperity and fame to Deptford and it set the tone of life there for many centuries. Parish registers from the 1590s onwards suggest that for every person who died in Deptford there were ten who

entrance to the King's Dockyard, 1840

came to the riverfront to get work or join their families. Besides shipwrights came those skilled in, or willing to learn, the many trades of a bustling waterfront town, including a rowdy population of sailors with tales of scurvy, starvation and overcrowding as well as tropical adventures and the oceans beyond the dreams of Creek or Thames.

Sir Francis Drake's ship, the *Golden Hind,* was lodged in a specially-constructed brick dock at Deptford on his return from his circumnavigation of the world in 1581. The ship was a tourist attraction for some decades and appears on a Dutch map as 'Captain Drackes schip', before it fell to pieces in the 1660s. Its final resting place was almost certainly within the dockyard site.

There were storehouses at Deptford Strand from the 15th century. Later known as the Red House, these were burnt down in 1639 and rebuilt in 1665 by the private contractor responsible for victualling the Fleet. With the new Red House as a central warehouse, Deptford had everything a merchant or sea captain could need. The official victualling

view near the Red House, 1771

depot was established on the site by the Navy Board in 1742. At this stage biscuit baking was the primary occupation though it would later expand into providing the fleet with pickled meat, rum, clothing and other supplies. By 1756 it had 60 employees ranging from Measurer of Bran & Small Coal to Senior Pastryman. In 1858 a visit by the Queen led to the yard being renamed the **Royal Victoria Victualling Yard.**

The dockyard continued to expand throughout the 16th and 17th centuries but was outstripped by other naval dockyards from the 18th century onwards due to the silting of the Thames. Between 1830 and 1844 it was only used for breaking up ships and was finally closed in October 1869. The Victualling Yard continued to serve the Navy until its closure in 1961. Some of the buildings were saved and converted as part of the development of Pepys Estate by the Greater London Council in the early 1960s.

Trinity House, which received its royal charter in 1514, grew from a medieval seamen's guild. The royal charter confirmed the guild's property held at Deptford, including local almshouses beside the Corporation's Hall near St Nicholas' Church. During the Armada threat of 1588 armour and weapons were stored there. The original buildings were demolished in 1786 and the almshouses rebuilt around a triangular green without the hall. In 1863 the inmates were moved and the almshouses were let to private tenants with their new neighbours, Rose Cottages, until the land was taken for extensions to Deptford Power Station. In 1672 new almshouses called Trinity Hospital were built around a garden to the east of Church Street. These 56 apartments for 'decayed seamen' or their widows were demolished in 1877. The hall was left standing and later let to the Temperance Society and the Salvation Army. Excavations have discovered the foundations of the almshouses and the garden soils of the quadrangle at the Church Street site.

Although the HQ of the Corporation moved in the 17th century, a grand procession came back to Deptford every Trinity Monday to elect a new Council. Landing at Deptford Green they would process to the Hall where the 'Loving Cup' was passed round with finger biscuits, before a trip to St Nicholas' Church for the customary sermon. The Duke of Wellington, Master from 1837, kept up the ceremony but it lapsed soon after his death in 1852 and the last Master to be elected in Deptford was Prince Albert, Victoria's husband.

site of the East India Company yard, 1840

The **East India Company** was formed in 1600 and ran its first voyages to the Far East from Deptford. In 1607 the Company leased the Stone Wharf at the end of Watergate Street from the Bridge House estate and soon took on other Bridge House lands at Church Marsh on the west part of the Power Station site. There it built a dry dock and slipways for shipbuilding along with an iron foundry, a spinning house, a slaughterhouse, storehouses and an isolated building on the east side to store gunpowder.

The Company's shipbuilder, William Burrell, lived on the west side. In the decade from 1610 the Company built over 30 ships at Deptford with a workforce of 500 men. The Company withdrew from Deptford in 1643 but continued to play an important role, leasing storage space at the Victualling Yard and having ships built in Deptford's private dockyards until the early 19th century.

E G Barnard's house at Deptford Green, circa 1840

The site continued as a private dockyard until the mid-19th century under a succession of shipbuilders including the Barnard family, who had a three-storey mansion house on Deptford Green. There were local complaints against E G Barnard, MP for Greenwich, for non-payment of poor rates on his shipyard at Deptford. He pleaded that the yard had been very little used recently and referred to himself as "a poor broken-down shipbuilder". By the 1850s the house at Deptford Green was in a ruinous condition.

There were many other **private yards** along the Deptford waterfront and shipbuilding also took place in the Norway Wharf area on the Greenwich side. There was a shipbuilding shed and slipway at Wood Wharf in 1777 and a fragment of Spanish amphora was recovered from the foreshore here.

Deptford Saints

The dedication of the ancient parish church to Saint Nicholas, the patron saint of mariners, shows local awareness of the hazards and insecurities of maritime life. Press-ganging, drowning, unemployment, disease and even an escaped tiger, were all part of life in a navy-building town.

On the old Dover road, Deptford's oldest hostelry was the Christopher, named for the patron saint of travellers. This pub, which existed at least from 1400, later became the Dover Castle and was the site of the 1989 and 1992 excavations which uncovered the Saxon burial ground.

early modern Creekside

The Broadway remained a focus of settlement, with the Old Draw Well in the centre of the road, the stocks, whipping post and prisoners' cage at the corner of Mill Lane, and a ducking stool installed at Deptford Bridge in 1688. Archaeological finds show the status of the area as a hub of trade. They include 16th and 17th century artefacts from the Rhineland, Normandy, Tuscany, Spain and the Netherlands, demonstrating Deptford's wide commercial contacts in this period.

Deptford Bridge was rebuilt several times after flooding. The rising waters of the Thames and the Creek led to frequent repairs to the river embankments overseen by the Sewer Commissioners. River walls and wharves continued to be increased in height. Late in the 17th century John Evelyn began to develop his land on the west side of Butt Lane (Deptford High Street) for housing, while the Bridge House Estate were doing

Deptford Broadway, 1840

the same in Church Field. Upper and lower Deptford remained quite separate. Ribbon development along the waterfront in the 16th and 17th centuries linked the earlier settlements into continuous chains which brought Deptford and London together by around 1700. Daniel Defoe commented in 1724 "the docks and building yards on the riverside between the town of Deptford and the streets of Redriff or Rotherhithe are effectually joined and the buildings daily increasing".

In the Great Plague of 1665 1,200 victims were buried in a pit prepared with lime in the north east corner of St Nicholas' churchyard. In 1697 the medieval church had become so dilapidated that the nave and chancel were demolished and rebuilt on the same foundations to house an expanded congregation. Provision for the dead was also expanded with brick vaults beneath the nave and the construction of the charnel house in 1701. The vaults were cleared of bodies in 1956.

Further population growth led to the division of the old medieval parish of Deptford into two parts and the building of a new church, consecrated in 1730. St Paul's was built on market garden land between Butt Lane and Church Street. The gardener, Samuel Priestman, was growing asparagus, gooseberries and fruit trees and was paid £80 compensation for the loss of his crop and £4 for dung. Building began in 1713 but was delayed by frost damage and the high water level. The Ravensbourne's catchment is very large.

Local bricklayer, Thomas Lucas, who had already begun to lay out and build the houses of Union Street (later Albury St), was responsible for the brick pillars and vaulted roof of the crypt. He also struggled to decipher Archer's strange plans for the Rectory. This was a three-pointed building with octagonal rooms and a large triangular staircase in the centre. The Rectory was dark and damp and needed frequent repairs. It was demolished in 1885, to be replaced by the Rectory Buildings tenement blocks and St Paul's Terrace of cottages which

St Paul's Church and Rectory, 1739

lasted until slum clearance in the early 1970s. The recent realignment of Crossfield Street by Lewisham Council with legacy funds from Deptford City Challenge has unfortunately destroyed any chance of bringing the Rectory foundations to light as an amenity.

There were gravel pits on both banks of the Ravensbourne in the 16th century and four acres of land called the Gravel Pits to the east of Church Street was common pasture for Deptford in 1608. This land was bought by John Addey's charity and became known as the Gravel Pits Estate. The Deptford Bridewell prison was built here in 1707 but closed in 1721. In 1726 the building was converted into a workhouse which served both the parishes of St Nicholas and St Paul until 1740 when the St Nicholas poor were transferred to the old manor house of Sayes Court. The St Paul's workhouse continued in use until 1846.

To the north of the Gravel Pits Estate lay the Copperas lands, where early dye and chemical manufacture was established by Sir Nicholas Crispe in the mid 17th century. Here copperas stones of iron pyrites from Kent and Essex were processed in copperas beds, 100ft trenches filled with rain water to produce red and black dyes. The works continued until the 1830s. Deptford's potteries were hit by the success of the Staffordshire potteries in the 18th century and forced to specialise in industrial pottery, sugar moulds, flower pots, chimney pots and crucibles, including Deptford Ware.

There were osier beds near the tide mill (zones F2, G, I1, I2, J1, J2) in 1576; south across the Creek in zone J1 in 1588; near the slaughterhouse in zones E2 and G and also in unspecified locations in 1608; around the peninsula on the east side of the Creek mouth in zones A1, A2 and A4 and on the west bank in zones B1 and B2 in 1777; and surviving into the 1840s adjacent to the tidemill and in zones B4 and B5. The early modern Creek was sufficiently friendly to wildlife to contain otters; one was shot here in 1684.

On the Deptford bank the Creekside area became known as 'the City'. Self-consciously separate from the rest of Deptford this was a small world with its own rules and customs, fiercely defensive of its boundaries. Around 1780, according to Dews, a bricklayer named Elder became the first 'Lord Mayor of Deptford' and started the yearly festivities known as Lord Mayor's Day. Passing through the streets of 'the city', he was saluted as 'My Lord Elder'. For many years he was accompanied by the Lady Mayoress, Bet Sedgewick, "whose character will not bear too close a scrutiny". Always over fond of a tipple, one day the Lady Mayoress was found dead in the street from drink. Elder's successor was a wit named Epsom, elected because he was "wise enough to puzzle the parson" and well known for giving impromptu pub speeches on subjects of international importance.

Lord Mayor's Day saw a great procession of sweeps, tinkers, dustmen and coal-heavers followed by the Lord and Lady on their donkeys and a long train of attendants in masks and tinsel. At Copperas Dock they took boats out in front of the old town before returning to their favourite pub, the Crispin and Crispiana, to finish the day. Dews tells how one time when the procession met the state barge of the Lord Mayor of London they persuaded him to pay homage of seven shillings to his local equivalent.

the royal dockyard with the grand 18th century enlargement of Henry VIII's storehouse

Pre-Construct Archaeology

Greenwich Reach: site of Deptford Power Station

The archaeological excavation carried out by Pre-Construct Archaeology on the site of the Deptford Power Station between August and November 1997 revealed structural remains of the Trinity House almshouses and the East India Company's Deptford dockyard. The work was commissioned by CGMS Ltd on behalf of their clients Fairview New Homes PLC in advance of the redevelopment of the site for housing.

remains of the Trinity House almshouses

The excavations focused on two areas, the first being adjacent to St Nicholas' churchyard by the Stowage where the Trinity House almshouses stood until the late 19th century. Although the Corporation of Trinity House was established in 1514, these almshouses were possibly founded in the previous century. Several discontinuous chalk wall footings and truncated internal floors were all that remained of these early buildings. Pins, needles and a thimble retrieved from this floor indicate one of the activities conducted in the room, while a 17th century token bearing the name 'Richard Finch' of 'Tour Streete' dates this activity.

Two new ranges of almshouse and a new hall were built during the 17th century and three brick buildings of this date were uncovered during the excavation. These had fireplaces and internal brick or tile floors with brick and cobbled yard surfaces and shallow open drains. These buildings had been modified, probably during the early 18th century, when one of the almshouse buildings was extended and the hall demolished although there appears to be no documentary record of this.

Pre-Construct Archaeology

17th century Thames river wall

Documentary records of the demolition of these buildings in 1786 and the rebuilding of the almshouses in 1788 were consistent with a second complex of brick almshouses discovered during excavation. These consisted of three large ranges, again built in brick, which formed a triangular courtyard complex. Internally these buildings each had a fireplace, with an adjacent brick floor and York stone slabs, although the majority of the floor appears to have been timber. The almshouses had an extensive drainage system with a small drain from each unit feeding into three main drain culverts which ran around the central courtyard area and then into an ablution block where the main culvert drained out into a drainage ditch on the marsh.

Three brick basemented buildings dating to the mid 19th century were found fronting onto the Stowage. These buildings, known as Rose Cottages, were not actually part of the almshouse complex which was itself let to private tenants after the removal of the last of the inmates in 1863. By 1895 the almshouses had all been demolished and they were soon followed by Rose Cottages.

The second area to be excavated was the site of the East India Company's Deptford dockyard. The Company was formed in 1600 and in 1614 it established a dockyard on part of Church Marsh leased from Bridge House. Here it built a dry dock, slipways and other facilities, although the Company's direct involvement there was over by 1626.

chalk and timber slipway from the 17th century, refurbished in the late 18th century

Pre-Construct Archaeology

The excavations revealed the possible remains of the medieval river embankment, established by the 13th century but probably with much earlier origins. The earliest structural survival was a timber revetment or river wall built to consolidate the embankment and prevent erosion. This was replaced by a more substantial structure some time later. Dendro-dating has proved that this was at the time of the East India Company's involvement.

Further developments during the 17th century included the construction of a deep wharf allowing larger boats to unload supplies or pull up to the dockyard edge for maintenance. Two substantial structures, probably the remains of the slipways upon which ships were built, were revealed alongside this wharf. Massive redevelopment of the dockyard, probably in the early 18th century, involved a new river wall being built at least 10m further north, reclaiming much land for the dockyard. This reorganisation also involved the enlargement of one of the slipways and the possible reconstruction of the second in a slightly new location.

Many of the timbers used in these structures were found to be re-used ship timbers, while others had either been roughed out in preparation for use or were offcuts of wood no longer required. Other interesting finds include masses of oakum or caulking hair, trenails, nails, wood chips and general debris from the shipbuilding industry. Large quantities of waste products from a pottery which occupied part of the site in the 18th century revealed information about another industry for which Deptford was once renowned.

excavation of Trinity almshouses in progress

Physalia Ltd

In the late 18th or early 19th century, at around the time that the pottery waste was being dumped, one of the slipways was again strengthened with a massive raft of chalk and timber, possibly reflecting the increased size of ships built at this time. This same slipway was yet again modified and partially rebuilt towards the end of the 19th century, remaining in use until at least 1910 although probably not for shipbuilding. It seems likely that this slipway outlived the dockyard, and may have been used for the delivery of coal by barge to the Ferranti Power Station built on the site in 1887-9.

industrial Creekside

In the early 19th century both sides of the Creek mouth had timber revetments with freestanding mooring posts on the west side. Hulks were moored here to house prisoners, and sick and disabled sailors. George Vancouver's ship the *Discovery* (often mistakenly thought to be Cook's ship of the same name) was moored off the Dockyard as a convict hulk in 1824. It was broken up in 1833 and replaced by the frigate *Thames*.

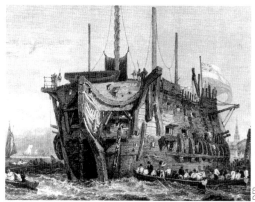

the Discovery as a convict hulk, 1826

The General Steam Navigation Company, formed by local timber merchant Thomas Brocklebank in 1820, established a shipyard on the west side of the Creek mouth in 1825, with Stowage House as the superintendent's residence. Here the company built and maintained its paddle steamers. They expanded throughout the century, acquiring the dry dock at Deptford Green. The company controlled the site until 1968 when it became a heavy lorry depot.

Other shipping industry included Lumley's yard at Deptford Green which built iron ships for the navy, colliers, steamers for Australia and sailing ships for the China trade. To the west was John Penn & Sons Marine Boiler and Engine Works at Payne's Wharf from 1825 to 1912. A six-bay arcade facade survives along the riverside and can be viewed from Deptford Beach at low tide. Ships were also built at Deptford Wharf and at Deptford Pier during the 19th century.

On the eastern banks the shipbuilding yard of J & G Rennie was established at Norway Wharf in 1859. In 1915 the yard with its sloping beach began to specialise in dredging, ship repairs and bargebuilding. The smaller yard at Wood Wharf had built and repaired the small wooden craft so typical of the Thames since the 18th century.

In the 18th century, a ferry operated across the mouth of the Creek from the Stairs at the Hoy Inn, then called the Peter Boat Alehouse. On the Greenwich side, the Wood Wharf beach at the end of Horseferry Road was the location for a series of ferries running to the Isle of Dogs. These culminated with the Great Greenwich Steam Ferry which opened in 1888, with its 270-ton landing stage which moved on rails up and down the foreshore with the tide.

pumping station and coal canopies, 1995

The Sewage Pumping Station on the east bank of the Creek was built in 1861 following a design competition. The Pumping Station raised sewage 18 feet so it could be passed to Crossness Works for treatment. The cast iron canopies which remain on the bank of the Creek were used for storing coal for the Pumping Station.

The Greenwich Gasworks were established in the 1820s and continued production until 1926. The other gas site, on the Deptford bank south of the railway, operated from 1836 until 1857 and the land still belongs to British Gas.

Other "noxious industries" spread along both sides of the Creek during the 19th century. In 1852 the *Kentish Mercury* listed the chemical works, breweries, bleach, dye and glue works, tar distilleries and manure manufactories which made the Creek area "one great stinking abomination". The gasworks at the mouth of the Creek let out their sulphurous pong and on Deptford Bridge Norfolk's Brewery and Holland's Distillery sent forth the sickly smell of hops and fermentation. In the very centre of Deptford the soap and candle factory in Regent Street (now Frankham Street) filled the air with "evil smells". The soapmaking tradition in the Deptford area dated back at least to the 1740s but it was a nasty business: the main ingredient was animal fat.

In 1856 Henry Pink the Medical Officer wrote to the local press about the impurities picked up by the Ravensbourne even before it reached the reservoirs of the Kent Waterworks near Mill Lane. The problems included "a large number of persons bathing in its waters...horses, waggons, carts and other vehicles constantly washed and cleansed in its stream...the practice of destroying cats and dogs...and the river is exposed to every contamination that mischievous or filthy persons may throw into it".

bridging the Creek

Deptford Bridge
A wooden bridge is known to have existed from the 1230s. In 1293 and 1345 there were discussions about the repair of Depevord bregge. At the east end of the bridge there was a chapel dedicated to St Katherine until 1548. The bridge was rebuilt partly in stone by 1570. Floods, such as the great storms of 1809 and 1824, often caused damage to the bridge which had to be repaired by the townspeople of Deptford and Greenwich.

Deptford Bridge, 1840

the Watermen's Woe - Creek Bridge
Small boats carrying passengers up and down and across the Thames had been a familiar sight for many centuries. The records of the Watermen's Company stretch back even before the terrible winter of 1281 when people crossed the icy Thames on foot between Lambeth and Westminster and the watermen were "very much distressed for want of their usual employment".

'Raising the Flap' at Creek Road bridge, 1932

The watermen fought a long war to protect their trade. In 1803 a company had been formed to build a bridge across the Creek near to its mouth at the Thames. Many watermen made their living ferrying people over the Ravensbourne at this point and they petitioned against it. The Act was passed and, though the watermen received some small compensation, they were forbidden to carry passengers over the water near to the new wooden footbridge. In 1815 a permanent lifting bridge suitable for carriages was built and the watermen had lost the battle.

the Railway Bridge and the Ha'penny Hatch
The third bridge to cut across the middle of the Creek with the arrival of the London & Greenwich Railway viaduct, the world's first urban railway, in 1836. In 1834 the *Greenwich Gazette* carried a letter from Common Sense who went out to take a look at the Greenwich Rail- Road works. He described Deptford as "one of the most rural places within a similar distance from London".

the railway viaduct with the 1963 lifting bridge

the Ha'penny Hatch footbridge and toll, 1890s (?)

For two years until 1838, the Ha'penny Hatch footbridge was the only way Greenwich passengers could board the new trains. Like Creek Bridge itself, the railway bridge had to lift to allow boats through. This took 12 men an hour to achieve until a new "most modern" structure was built in 1963 – this is the imposing landmark which straddles the site today. Unfortunately it was welded shut in the early 1970s. The Ha'penny Hatch footbridge remained in place until the early 1930s and no records have been found to explain its disappearance. The dangers and frustrations of a pedestrian trip between Deptford and Greenwich led to the development of the project to replace the footbridge and reforge the historic link between the two towns.

The closure of the royal dockyard marked the end of Deptford as a navy-building town but "Deptford was industry and industry was Deptford...No economist would despise Deptford, although many preferred to say they lived anywhere but in Deptford." (Charles Buckley). The Foreign Cattle Market opened on the site in 1871, turning the old covered slipways into sheep pens and cattle sheds. Being "in the meat trade" became locally respectable, at least for husbands

central shed at the Foreign Cattle Market

bringing home regular wages. The Gut Girls, who cleaned the offal from the carcasses, were considered disreputable and became a focus for high-society moralising philanthropy.

Soon another industrial development put Deptford back on the map. The young genius of electric power, Sebastian di Ferranti, chose Creekside for his new Power Station, the first large-scale power generator in the world. Born in Liverpool, Ferranti went to University College London at 16 but had to give it up when his father became ill. He worked at Siemens in Woolwich, inventing a number of revolutionary electrical devices which both increased efficiency and could be manufactured at a fraction of the previous cost. He soon had his own company making alternators, arc lamps, meters and other of his inventions. In 1885 he patented the high voltage AC transformer system which is basically still in use today.

For most people lighting was provided by candles and paraffin lamps. The Blackpool illuminations had begun in 1879 but the gas companies reassured their shareholders that "the electric light can never be applied indoors without the production of an offensive smell which undoubtedly causes headaches". Nevertheless small local stations were set up in the West End and by 1881 the House of Commons itself was lit by electricity.

Ferranti planned a big power station capable of supplying all London, built on cheap land beyond the city and with the unlimited cooling potential of the Thames. The largest existing engine was 750 hp; the Deptford plant would have four of 10,000 hp each. The boilers would have 70 times more capacity and the four 500-ton alternators produced 10,000 volts.

The new station would supply two million lamps. With Ferranti's advice the London Electric Supply Corporation Ltd was established and bought three acres at the Stowage on the site of the East India Company's yard. According to Ferranti's wife, Gertrude Ince: "The first thing I remember during those first months of married life was Deptford, and again Deptford. We talked Deptford and dreamed Deptford."

Ferranti's power station at Deptford, 1889

Ferranti staked his reputation, his fortune and many long months of labour to make the Deptford dream come true. Eminent men of the time prophesied disaster. He wanted to use 10,000 volts; they said more than 2,000 was dangerous. Thomas Edison visited the station during construction and told the press the risks but he added "Oh, it will go!" In the early 20th century Deptford expanded from lighting to transport with contracts for the LCC tramways and the suburban service of the London, Brighton & South Coast Railway. Other railways joined the network and the complexity of Deptford's electrical systems increased so much that it was said the station could "link up to anything – even the Gas Works!".

The Station was expanded to the west in 1926 and in 1948-53 the Deptford East (High Pressure) Station brought it to the bank of the Creek mouth. There was a friendly rivalry between Deptford East and West but whichever side you were on, 'the Light' was a good place to work, with reasonable wages, security and companionable conditions. For some there was also the possibility of a flat in St Nicholas' House, built by the London Power Co.

In 1938 precautions were taken against the coming war with air raid covers installed over the switch house. There were still workers who remembered the 1916 Zeppelin bombing which killed a man on site, but nothing prepared them for the tragedies of the blitz. Altogether 27 staff were killed on site by enemy action, the highest number of any power station in the country and testimony to Deptford's crucial position and purpose.

extension of the Landing Stage for barges bringing coal to the power station, 1936.

When Dunstan Thompson visited Deptford in 1947, he saw the power station as "a giant complex of stone supporting two chimneys, 20 storeys high, made to look like colossal Doric columns...monstrous and magnificent. I thought of what a ruin it would some day make." Closure and demolition began in the 1960s; the last part was demolished and the site completely flattened in 1992.

impacts of development

The topographical features of Creekside, most obviously the Thames and the Creek itself but also the road layout, are key to the historical continuity of the area. Unfortunately some of these have recently been obliterated by development and 'regeneration'. Crossfield Street, the diagonal link between High Street and Church Street, which can be seen on the earliest maps, has been realigned with public money. The characteristic S-shape of the Stowage has been smoothed out as part of the Fairview New Homes development. The road Creekside suffers from heavy traffic, particularly associated with the waste transfer depot and has recently lost some of its definition through DLR demolition works.

the realignment of the ancient Crossfield St

The raised viaduct of the railway, slicing through the area on its 878 brick arches, is protected by listing yet the footpath which once stretched along the whole length from Greenwich to London Bridge is almost entirely inaccessible at present. The new feature of the DLR viaduct, which has destroyed some sections of the historic fabric, has yet to be absorbed into the landscape, but Creekside is familiar with large-scale infrastructure and no doubt it will soon become part of everyday Deptford and West Greenwich.

Creekside's most historic site, the Creek mouth to St Nicholas' Church, has been home to Trinity House, the East India Company, the General Steam Navigation Company and Ferranti's Power Station, as well as numerous private shipyards. The evolved layout of this legacy has has been wiped clear, the land scraped and the archaeological remains destroyed to an extent not matched even by the huge piles of the Power Station buildings. With the dream of maritime power gone and its related industries dead, Fairview's new homes will be the inheritance we pass to the third millennium. The site is being marketed as Millennium Quay and the rumoured new street names (Basavi St and Glacier St) have no local relevance. However, efforts to save and renovate the Landing Stage may ensure one survivor of Ferranti's vision.

the Fairview site in progress

On the site of the royal dockyard, Henry VIII's storehouse (enlarged in the 18th century) and the famous clocktower was demolished in 1981 for more Convoys warehousing. The sole survivor of the pre-19th century dockyard, the building known as the Master Shipwright's House or the Shipwright's Palace, has recently been purchased for renovation as a private residence.

There are plans on the Greenwich bank to move the boat-based industry of Prior's Aggregates southwards, freeing up a swathe of development land for mixed residential and office use, while on the Deptford bank the waste transfer depot is the subject of an arts lottery bid for a new Laban dance centre. On Creek Road the Rachel McMillan College Building is empty. Mumford's Mill still stands majestic but practically derelict on a skyline which once thronged with mills.

mills at the Creek head in the 1970s, all gone now except Mumford's (far right)

Reconstruction of the Creek walls by riparian owners is being guided by the Environment Agency to ensure proper flood defence, guard against encroachment and encourage ecological enhancement where possible. Unfortunately but inevitably, the oldest walls are those most in disrepair and the arguments against encroachment win out against either historical or ecological value.

There are some projects being promoted or funded through local regeneration programmes which use the historical legacy of Creekside as inspiration for developments which will meet the needs of current and future residents. Mainly local community initiatives, these include the reinstatement of the Ha'penny Hatch bridge, the restoration of the Thames barge *Niagara* as part of the community boatyard project, the renovation of the Landing Stage within the Thames Path, environmental improvements and new gates to St Nicholas' churchyard, and the proposed McMillan Centre for Children and Families in the Rachel McMillan Building.

Deptford beach and the Landing Stage

further research

There are many ways in which the history of Creekside could be explored further. The Bridge House deeds at the Corporation of London Record Office offer insights into the medieval layout and usage of settlements, fields and marshlands. The records of the Surrey and Kent Commissioners of Sewers show early river walls, drainage channels and marshes. The development of the East India Company site can be traced through the Company's court minutes held at the India Office. Crucial to the interpretation of the area between Creek Road, Church Street, the railway and the Creek are deeds relating to the Copperas lands, including a map of 1674, are held at the Surrey Record Office. To the south, the Gravel Pits estate will be illuminated by the Addey & Stanhope records, recently acquired by Lewisham Local Studies Library. Land tax assessments, parish rate books and directories held locally show the occupation of each area by various trades and industries in the 18th and 19th centuries. It would be useful to collate borehole and test-pit logs for a wider area and compare Creekside with studies elsewhere in the Lower Thames region. There are also some fascinating characters for biographical research: the martyr vicar of St Nicholas' Richard Wyche, the genius Sebastian de Ferranti and the unfortunate Samuel Scott, to name just three.

The survey of Deptford High Street by the Royal Commission of Historic Monuments of England found that the buildings of the period 1660-1800 are varied in nature, small scale and irregular. They are broadly classifiable as artisanal housing the like of which does not survive elsewhere in London. Internal layouts and joinery details on upper storeys are of particular interest, providing much information about original living arrangements. The survey identified dates of construction and early occupants. Though humble these building have great significance. The study has made it possible to address heretofore unanswerable questions about the range of low status housing options in and around Georgian London, variety and standardisation in vernacular housing and the endurance of supposedly 17th century forms into the 18th century.

The social life of Creekside has hardly been touched in this description, yet offers a rich field for study and many themes which remain relevant today. The work of the McMillan sisters is currently being researched for a publication in 1999 by the McMillan Legacy Group. The Albany Institute was located in Creekside for over 80 years and deserves its own history. The Deptford Theatre at the corner of Church Street and Creekside, later the Oxford Arms and now the Birds Nest public house (and theatre, and Thai restaurant, and festival beer bus), would also merit fuller study.

The story of public housing can be told through Creekside's five estates. Hughesfield includes some of the earliest London County Council blocks, while Haddington is a typically grim and run-down estate potentially due for demolition under the Time for Greenwich SRB. Meridian Estate, in a prime location on the Greenwich waterfront, suffers the most intense development pressure. Sayes Court is a small 1960s GLC estate on the Deptford side. Perhaps the most unusual housing story is that of Crossfield Estate.

the Crossfield story

Most of the Crossfield blocks were built by the LCC in the late 1930s and were under GLC management until April 1971 when they were handed over to Lewisham Council. The GLC Housing Department was famous for its grand schemes but notorious on matters of day-to-day housing management. Conditions in the blocks were appalling. One woman said "I have lived on this estate for 22 years and spent 21 of them trying to get out". Crossfield referrals to Social Services for material poverty were four times the local average.

With advice from GLC traffic engineers, Lewisham Council were planning to turn Church Street into a major dual carriageway. Crossfield tenants, some of them living

within feet of the proposed road, had not been consulted or even told about the plans. When Albany community worker Ann Gallagher called a tenants' meeting in January 1973, the reaction was instant. The long-brewed anger at conditions was given expression in mobilising support for the demolition of the whole estate. They produced a brochure describing the effects of the road - danger, noise and isolation from the rest of Deptford - and their everyday experience of blocked drains, rats, damp and fungus. They also took direct disruptive action with a demonstration closing Church St to traffic during Friday evening rush hour in the middle of a rail strike.

Graham Maxwell @ Othens

While other councillors had walked out of early meetings, the Crossfield group found weighty support in Ron Pepper, chair of the Planning Committee and the two young councillors Nick Taylor and Nick Gregory. Despite concern that demolition was a waste of housing stock, the councillors supported tenants in their campaign as well as taking up individual cases. Within two months of the first meeting the Housing Committee agreed to rehouse all the tenants on the estate.

A triumph of local activism, but the story does not end there. A group called Student Co-operative Dwellings had approached Cllr Ron Pepper with a proposal to take over Crossfield. This fell by the wayside but it gave Pepper the idea of using the estate to house single professional people. Head of a Peckham secondary school, he was acutely aware of the teacher shortage in schools crowded with the children of the early 1960s baby bulge. Places at Crossfield were offered to ILEA, Goldsmiths College and Thames Polytechnic (now the University of Greenwich).

A new community began to grow up in the blocks: a constantly-shifting population of students, artists, musicians, teachers and social workers. The new Crossfield brought the public sector into Deptford, where its workers lived with the same facilities and often worse conditions than their pupils or clients. The estate created an 'integrated' middle class segment without the gentrification or widespread displacement of working class communities seen in the rest of docklands. It also gave an unprecedented momentum to the development of a radical community arts and music scene. Dire Straits, Squeeze and the Flying Pickets were the ones who made it beyond Deptford but there was also a "proliferation of tiny groups, growing and splitting like amoeba, producing discs from garage studios sounding like they've been cut in a biscuit tin." (*Time Out*, 1978).

With only minimum improvements, the blocks were far from normal standards of accommodation and it was made clear that when families started to form they would be rehoused elsewhere in Deptford. This maintained the rather artificial uniformity of the Crossfield population right through the 1970s. At the end of the Labour years, Lewisham Council were successful in flooding the Department of Environment with proposals for housing so Government restrictions on new Council building did not finally catch up until the end of 1981. The steep decline in available property which followed made it almost impossible for people with children to get transfers out of Crossfield after 1982. During the 1990s the situation has come full circle. The better job prospects of the second wave allowed them more options than their predecessors, and those who stay do so because they love the area.

Crossfield has retained a very high level of community activism which, properly tapped, could be of great value to the regeneration of Creekside.

*f*oreshore heritage

The **Museum of London Archaeology Service** identified thirteen principal features within the Creek channel.

α**101** Timber river wall. Hilton's Wharf. 1844-68. Portions have been constructed later, possibly associated with infilling of a dock/inlet in 1876-94.

α**102** Timber river wall. Salter's Paper. 1844-68. Large-scale build up of mud and detritus. Sluice or drain access gate above this line shows accumulation may predate the insertion of the wall.

α**103** Timber river wall. Behind Drake House. 1844-68. Gap in wall exposes consolidation dumping behind the wall once it was built.

α102. timber river wall with drain access gate

α104. railway bridge with earlier masonry bed (α105)

α**104** Rail bridge, part of the listed railway viaduct and an imposing local landmark. Built with central 8m drawbridge in 1838, Replaced in 1884 and replaced again with the present lifting bridge in 1963. The Ha'penny Hatch footbridge ran along its south side until it was removed, probably in the 1930s.

α**105** Masonry river bed lining under rail bridge. 1838?. They are not keyed into the neater masonry finish of the present bridge structure and in some cases stones appear to have been smashed at their junction with the abutments – could indicate that the bed pre-dates the present bridge piles.

α**106** Dock or inlet. Gas Alley. 1876-94. Formed from brick walls with timber uprights, along alignment of railway.

α**107** Remains of timber revetment. ?pre-1750. At least 26 upright round timbers, line extending for at least 7m. Probably a revetment to the west bank of the Creek (faithful replication of the curve of the modern bank could indicate that the Creek has been widened westward in this area). Date of construction unknown, could be as early as medieval period.

α**108** Barge-bed revetment (includes a109-112). 1868. Series of stout timber posts retaining a wall of planks laid horizontally on edge. These retained a series of planks on end. Formed a platform alongside the cast-iron river wall of the sewage pumping station (built 1861). Majority of platform is consolidated rubble. Shelves gently at 0.4–0.5m above Creek bed. Since the cast-iron coal sheds survive nearby it is likely that coal barges moored here during deliveries to the pumping station. Currently 73.9m long, 7–10m wide. Original plans of 1861 show it as 140m long.

α106. *British Gas Transco inlet with beach*

α107. *remains of Creek revetment, possibly pre-1750*

α**109** Masonry and timber splash apron for pumping station outfall pipe. 1868. Formed a thin T-shape from river wall to barge-bed revetment and along the side of the revetment. The stem of the T was directly beneath a cast-iron drain outfall. Masonry in various types of stone sett, including granite. Deliberate use of different natural colours for decorative effect "an extraordinary attention to detail considering that the role of the structure was to deflect water from the sewage station outfall away from the barge-bed fabric".

α**110** Masonry and timber drain. At southern end of splash apron. ?1868. Runs parallel with the apron toward the river wall, a timber-framed ceramic drain topped with further masonry setts. Emptied into the Creek below the level of the barge-bed surface, could have been a foul service.

α**111** Timber barge-bed revetment. 1868. Part of the overall structure but south of a change in the pumping station river wall.

α**112** Masonry and timber splash apron. 1868. Similar to α109 but without the T-shape, instead a simple perpendicular line to the river wall.

α**113** Square timber uprights in the centre of the present Creek bed. Form a crude line roughly parallel with west bank and may once have been a revetment or river wall. Possibly remnants of the pre-18th century river wall line.

α108. *surveying the Pumping Station outfall apron*

rubbish

The most frequent comment about Deptford Creek, and indeed Deptford itself, has been that it is 'dirty' and 'full of rubbish'. With the decline of industry, the waters of the Creek are actually far cleaner than they have been for centuries. Twice a day, however, the tide brings the silt-laden North Sea surging up the Thames and into the Creek, giving both rivers their characteristic brown colouring.

One cannot deny the accusation that the Creek is strewn with rubbish and it is one of the aims of the Creek Environment Project to address this problem. In order to do this it was important to survey the rubbish, classify the types and origins, consider the impacts and make recommendations for its removal.

The survey was undertaken by **Mike Canty**, a resident boater. A practical man who will brook no nonsense, Mike has become surprisingly philosophical, arguing from first principles about the nature of 'rubbish' itself. While the rubbish has little negative impact on the wildlife of the Creek, it can be a severe danger to navigation and it encourages the human perception of low value which results in a cycle of continued dumping. The survey work has informed all discussions for the future stewardship of the Creek.

techniques

The Creek was divided into 22 distinct areas, each of very different character.
The channel bed was walked, measured and photographed at low tide over a period of 100 hours. Large items were labelled for identification and monitoring.
The study identified five categories of rubbish:
historic rubbish – forgotten or mislaid items that have been dropped accidently into the Creek
industrial waste – bricks and other materials from yards backing onto the Creek
industrial flytipping – materials and waste oil deliberately taken to the river and discarded
individual flytipping – discarded fridges, hoovers, carpets, garden waste, bicycles
amusement waste – throwing in a paving slab, car tyre or shopping trolley, not as cost-free waste disposal but in order to watch the splash.

findings

The areas downstream are almost entirely clear of any debris, since they tend to be washed out with the tide. As the railway bridge is approached from the north, the first large clutters of rubbish begin to be evident. They include motor vehicle panels, bumpers and mechanical parts at the back of Brookmarsh Industrial Estate; bricks, salt-glazed pipe and reinforcing mesh at Graham's Builders Yard; and scaffolding rods beside Kent Scaffolding. This area also sees the first clusters of shopping trolleys and their attendant tangles of carpet and plastic waste forming unnatural shoals in the river bed.

The area south from the railway bridge is mainly clear as far as Theatre Arm where a massive tangle of around 50 trolleys have created a barrage across the mouth of the arm. From this arm, around Bookers' Cash & Carry and up to the two sills, almost the entire river bottom is a mass of shoals, generated by several hundred trolleys and a range of household discards.

life of the Creek

the thin green line

Deptford Creek is a land of extremes. At high tide the brackish water laps up to a green belt of vegetation that rapidly gives way to the built environment. At low tide it is quite another beast. It is Deptford's grand canyon, getting deeper and grander as you proceed towards the Thames. As the tidal waters retreat towards the North Sea a shallow trickle of freshwater is exposed meandering down the middle, flanked by the rich mud and shingle banks of the foreshore.

Few natural riverine features now survive in Deptford Creek. Like the Thames throughout inner London, it has been *cabin'd, cribb'd, confin'd,* over the centuries as land has been 'gained' (taken) from the river. The effect of this has been to push the tide further up river, making it progressively narrower, deeper and faster.

The Creek is the only tributary south of the Thames in inner London which remains relatively intact. The only other river that is still open to the sky at the Thames confluence is the Wandle, but the tidal nature of the Wandle delta has been affected by the construction of a half barrage. All the rivers in between have been covered over. The Falcon, Neckinger, and Effra survive only as road names in the urban matrix.

Ecologically Deptford Creek is in better condition now than it has been for at least a hundred years. This is despite the fact that to date no works to the Creek or its walls have ever taken wildlife into account. This recovery is largely due to three factors which have coincided over the last few decades: the improvement in water quality, the partial abandonment of the Creek, and decay.

Since the 1950s, when untreated sewage was still discharged into the river, pollution control has been tightened up. From supporting no fish then, today the Thames supports over 100 species of fish, including salmon. The remarkable recovery of the Thames and its tidal tributaries resulted in its designation as a Site of Metropolitan Importance for Nature Conservation by the London Ecology Unit in 1986. It is now internationally renowned as one of the cleanest urban rivers in the world. Ironically, few Londoners are aware of this; the river is still perceived as 'dirty' by many.

the thin green line

Deptford Creek has been a quiet backwater for decades. The survey process has been a little like finding the *Marie Celeste*. There is evidence of past activity, but the workers have packed up their tools and gone, the old salts and ships frequent other docks and wharves. The landowners both sides of the Creek have turned their backs on it and use the roads instead. It has been abandoned and left to decay; this glorious decay has allowed nature to move back in. There are two exceptions to this general process. Prior's Aggregates still bring in sand and aggregates by boat. Further up the Creek barges are still repaired by local resident boatowners.

The habitats of Deptford Creek are difficult to classify. Overall, it could perhaps best be described as a watery wasteland, with the word wasteland denoting, as it often does, a diverse range of habitats which are species rich and locally distinct. The historic development of the Creek has produced variations in surface topography and the variety of artificial and natural substrates, coupled with the tidal nature of Deptford Creek, has led to the development of a bewildering array of habitat types and specific niches.

Nick Bertrand

The intertidal foreshore is crucial to the estuary in ecological terms. It is here that fish spawning grounds are found and where the most abundant algal and invertebrate communities occur. These, in turn, provide food for birds, other invertebrates and fish. In the Creek the intertidal zone is certainly biologically diverse but it is limited in the space it occupies, being confined by the vertical sea walls. The seasonal fluctuations of algae paint the walls and foreshore in a constantly changing palette of bronzes and greens with every receding tide. As the tide comes in again, tubifex worms, in their millions, poke their heads up through the mud and are 'grazed' by ducks and fish. The brackish nature of the Creek waters means that marine common shrimps can co-exist here with the freshwater mayfly.

The vertical sea walls support over 120 plant species. This is quite rare along the intertidal zone in inner London; there are few places where wild vegetation is tolerated at all. The flora here include an international mix of species reflecting London's trading, imperial and gardening past.

Walking down the canyon at low tide can feel like being in a rainforest. The vegetation is mostly high up in the canopy. It radiates out on linear branches (ledges) from the tree trunks (rubbing posts), it pokes out like epiphytes from any nook and cranny it can exploit. Buddleja and garden angelica are most noticeable and contribute to the unique flavour of the Creek. On closer inspection oddities such as a mature wild fig tree and saplings of evergreen and Turkey oaks growing from the rotting timbers are revealed. At high tide plants such as Japanese rose and hemlock water-dropwort can be seen in full flower underwater as if they would be pollinated by fish.

Nick Bertrand

Penny Metal

The Creek is a haven for birds: over sixty species have been recorded. Unusually, moorhens who normally nest at the water's edge here build nests in buddleja bushes hanging over the Creek just above high water, to avoid the nest being inundated. It is one of the few places in the country where you can see the nationally rare and elusive black redstart, singing from cranes, foraging on the aggregate piles and the foreshore before returning to its nest in a derelict building or even the middle of a building site. The regionally rare polypody fern clings to the cliff-like walls of the imposing Mumford's Mill, which is also home to a family of kestrels who have been seen hunting the feral pigeons with whom they share the building.

Most of the adjacent land is either too intensively managed or highly developed to allow much habitat to develop. However, there are areas within this built-up environment which wildlife is still utilising. These habitats go under a variety of pseudonyms, the latest being 'brownfield sites', but are perhaps best known simply as wastelands.

Wastelands are the classic city habitat, unique to their locality. Cosmopolitan in nature, they reflect the history of how the city has developed and are an intimate part of the local character. They contain an international community of plants reflecting the international community of people living here. They are incredible places. Sites that have a history of devastating things being done to them such as bulldozing. Then, when people have turned their backs for a time, wildlife comes steaming in, transforming spoliated places into extraordinary diverse habitats. The impact of people on these sites is *more by their presence than their skill*. People do not set out to establish the right conditions for wildlife. It is an inadvertent consequence of their actions. This is also how other now highly valued habitats, such as moorland and heathland, originally came about.

A walk down the Creek at low tide is a special experience where the unexpected often happens. The startling iridescence of a kingfisher is glimpsed darting up river or perched on a shopping trolley. Hundreds of Chinese mitten crabs (originally introduced in the ballast of visiting ships) lurk under discarded carpets, hub caps and old doors in the mud banks. The annual migration upstream of young flounder in huge numbers during May can be seen as they flurry to escape being trodden on.

Deptford Creek is at a cusp. Within a very narrow window of time it and the land adjacent to it has or will be impacted upon severely. There is the DLR extension and the major redevelopment of the Deptford Power Station site, Greenwich Reach East, Hilton's Wharf, and the waste transfer depot, as well as the replacement of several sea walls. Almost the whole of the lower Creek, most of the middle Creek and parts of the upper Creek will be affected within a five-year time frame. The consequences are difficult to calculate for any one of these developments; for all of them combined, impossible. We will have to rely on everything possible being done by the agencies involved and the resilience of our wildlife communities. What they need most is space and a bit of privacy. These are somewhat at a premium in this area.

planning policy guidance

Deptford Creek is part of the Tidal Thames Site of Metropolitan Importance for Nature Conservation (site M31) as designated by the London Ecology Unit (1986). It falls within two planning authorities – Greenwich and Lewisham. It is designated a Site of Nature Conservation Importance in the Greenwich UDP (1994), although the Creek is not specifically referred to, or shown as such on the Proposals Map. In the Lewisham UDP (1996) the Creek is specifically identified as an Area of Nature Conservation Importance. Policies within both UDPs are in place to protect and conserve sites of nature conservation importance.

Recent planning guidance has improved the protection of Sites of Metropolitan Importance. RPG 3 *Strategic Guidance for London Planning Authorities* 1996 requires that they should be treated in the same way as Sites of Special Scientific Importance in the context of development control. RPG 3B/9B *Strategic Planning Guidance for the River Thames* 1997 further reinforces the importance of the tidal Thames and its ecology. It recommends that local authorities should:

- develop proposals and include policies to protect, conserve and enhance natural landscapes along the river
- seek assessments of the likely effect of proposed development proposals on the ecology of the river where these seem likely to have significant impact
- discourage land infill and development which encroaches into the river and its foreshore other than in exceptional circumstances and should consult the Environment Agency and the Port of London Authority about any such proposals.

In addition, the Wildlife & Countryside Act 1981 provides legal protection for certain species. Two species present on the Creek – black redstart and kingfisher – are listed on Schedule 1. This protects them (including eggs and nestlings) from disturbance during breeding, taking from the wild, injury, killing or sale, except where it is the incidental result of a lawful operation and cannot be reasonably avoided.

Land drainage consent must be sought from the Environment Agency for works in, on or over the Creek and within 16m of the banks. Wildlife habitats are considered when the EA makes its decisions. All works on navigational tidal waterways are covered by Port of London Authority river works licenses. The Ministry of Agriculture, Fisheries & Food (MAFF) controls any works which could cause pollution to watercourses. Local authorities require planning applications for any major structural changes, including pontoons.

The Biodiversity Action Plan process, which started in London in 1996, should help to further identify species and habitats of regional and local importance to the capital (such as the black redstart in the case of the Creek) and implement means to protect them at policy level. However in London the major gap that needs filling is that between policy and practice.

mud and water

The physical and chemical characteristics of Deptford Creek are constantly changing. Water and silt enter the Creek both from the river Ravensbourne and from the Thames estuary as the tides push in twice a day. Historically, the Creek was home to many potentially polluting industries and today there are still car breakers, a waste depot and aggregate companies on its banks. For this reason, and to establish baseline information, two studies on the physical and chemical composition of the sediments and waters of the Creek were undertaken by the **University of Greenwich** in 1996/97. Soil from the British Gas Transco site adjacent to the Creek was also analysed for evidence of contamination. Additional information is provided from previous studies by the National Rivers Authority.

techniques

Water was sampled at high and low tide while both shallow and deep samples of the exposed sediments were taken. Water samples were measured for pH, conductivity, temperature, dissolved oxygen content and total suspended solids (TSS). The percentage organic matter (POM) and toluene extractable fraction (TEF) of sediment and soil samples were ascertained. TEF gives an estimate of the abundance of organic substances such as tars, oils and phenols. In the laboratory, various analytical techniques were used, including flame photometry, atomic absorption spectrophotometry,

chemical testing in the laboratory

Physalia Ltd

potentiometric stripping voltametry and inductively coupled plasma-optical emission spectrometry. Baseline information was established for 18 metals, 5 anions (nutrients) and 11 Polycyclic Aromatic Hydrocarbons (PAHs). The metals and anions which were investigated all occur naturally in the environment but pollution can lead to elevated levels which may be harmful to living organisms. PAHs are indicative of activities which produce wastes which are highly persistent or toxic in nature.

findings

physical characteristics

The waters of the Creek are neutral or slightly alkaline with a clear salinity gradient due to the inflow of freshwater. Even at low tide, however, the water is slightly brackish. The silt-laden high tide waters were found to have over 10 times as much TSS as the water at low tide. Temperatures were within the normal range with no evidence of excessively high temperatures from discharges into the Creek. The dissolved oxygen content was relatively high for an urban estuary and highest in winter when water temperatures are lower.
The POM of the mud flats was generally lower than that found in soils on dry land with higher readings in the upstream sections and especially in the top layers of mud. Overall, TEF levels were low showing little evidence of heavy organic contamination but three 'warm spots' were found close to former polluting industries.

metals

The most commonly occurring metals in the sediments and waters of the Creek were the 'beneficial' metals; Sodium, Iron, Calcium and Potassium. Of the potentially harmful metals, only Zinc was present at levels high enough to cause concern and even these levels were not excessive. Overall, levels of metals were at the lower end of the scale for urban or industrialised estuaries.

nutrients

Chloride was over ten times higher at high tide and twice as high downstream near the Thames, reflecting the higher salinity of the incoming tidal waters. Nitrate levels were higher in the Creek (especially in winter) than in the Ravensbourne but well below European Union safe limits for human consumption and wildlife. Estuaries often show high nitrate levels due to the high deposition and breakdown of detritus and organic waste. High nitrate levels could cause mild eutrophication but other factors such as the very low phosphate levels probably prevent this.

PAHs

Only benzo(a)pyrene, which can be highly toxic and carcinogenic was present at levels which could cause concern. However PAHs are extremely water repellent and become attached to mud particles, so they are unlikely to be readily bioavailable. Readings for the gasworks site were lower than expected suggesting that, either the site was used only for storage and not the production of gas or, that the site has been capped with soil from elsewhere.

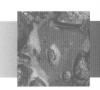

impacts of development

Dredging could release pollutants trapped in the deep mud back into the environment. Although levels of metals in deep mud were nowhere found to be high, further detailed investigations should be undertaken prior to any dredging because of the possibility of localised hot-spots.

mud glorious mud

Encroachment would minimise the available area of ecologically rich foreshore and cause changes in water flow and patterns of sediment deposition. Encroachment should be avoided if at all possible in line with current EA policy.

Large items of rubbish in the Creek bed currently allow more variation in the flow of water leading to more dissolved oxygen. Some mitigation measures should be provided if they are to be removed.

algae

Algae are a very large and successful group of plants which flourish in water or in damp places on land. Many of them are single-celled and therefore only visible with a microscope, although in a mass they can be very conspicuous. Some consist of fine threads or filaments. Others develop into large plants like sea kelp (most seaweed is actually algae).

The solid and sediment surfaces in Deptford Creek provide habitats for both macroalgae and microalgae. Due to the Creek's tidal nature both freshwater and marine algae grow and flourish there.

There are three main types of macroalgae, defined by their colours. Red algae are mainly marine species, often growing in deep water. Brown algae are also mostly marine species. They are characterised by their brown pigment caused by the chemical *fucoxanthin* which turns green if plunged into hot water. Green algae are found in marine, freshwater and damp terrestrial habitats and almost certainly gave rise to the first land plants 430 million years ago. Other types of algae include blue-green and yellow-brown.

Microalgae include diatoms which are single-celled organisms with a distinctive two-part shell. The two halves fit together, one on top of another like a box and its lid. The extremely delicate markings of these shells are used by microscopists to test the quality of their lenses. Diatoms first became abundant some 100 million years ago and have been found as fossils. Many of these fossil species are identical to those still living today which shows a rare persistence through time.

techniques

The algal survey was carried out by the **Natural History Museum**. Algae were sampled at three sites in the Creek in October 1997:
Site 1 (Zone A2, west bank)
Vertical wood and stone wall with wood piling and shuttering; foreshore of soft alluvial mud. Algae growing on nearby concrete steps were also sampled. At this site it was possible to access the sediment at different tidal levels.
Site 2 (Zone D3, west bank)
Vertical brick wall; foreshore of soft mud.
Site 3 (Zone B2, east bank)
Vertical wall, concrete at the top and wood lower down; foreshore of soft mud.

Where access allowed, macroalgae samples were taken at intervals along a line from high water level to foreshore level.

Sediment samples were taken for microalgae by marking three areas at each site with a tube and removing the surface sediment within these rings. In the laboratory the sediment was transferred to petri dishes and allowed to settle, with any excess water carefully removed. Lens tissue was placed on the surface overnight and then placed in a sterile marine medium with a few drops of Lugol's iodine to preserve the microalgae. The samples were analysed under a microscope (x40) to calculate both cell density and the contribution of each species to the assemblage.

findings

macroalgae

Ten species of benthic (deep-living) macroalgae were recorded in Deptford Creek in October 1997. These green, brown, yellow-green and blue-green algae are all typical of brackish waters like the Thames. The overall diversity of macroalgae in the Thames is limited by the low salinity of the river water. In the Creek, the uniformity of the macroalgae vegetation reflects the lack of variety of habitats.

Nick Bertrand

algae growing on a post in the Creek

Zonation refers to the bands of plant life found at different levels vertically on the wall, reflecting the preferences of particular species for different tidal conditions. Some walls show these bands more clearly than others; site 3 was the most obvious. At all three sites the moss *Tortula muralis* formed a band of vegetation just above high water level while the alga *Rhizoclonium riparium* tended to be found at the base of the wall.

microalgae

Although some people do not consider the Creek mud to be attractive, the soft sediments provide ideal habitat for microalgae including diatoms. Algae are an important component in marine and estuarine biodiversity. They offer important habitat, are primary producers and provide nutrition for many animals. They are food for invertebrates which, in turn, attract wading and shore birds to the area.

The mud layer in the Creek has a golden brown appearance and is dominated by motile diatoms. There was a considerable diversity of diatoms (63 species). Most species found were typical of brackish and marine habitats but some typically freshwater species were found in low numbers, probably washed into the site from upstream.

Different species were dominant at different sites. *Nitzschia gracilis* was dominant towards the Thames but lessened dramatically at the south end of the Creek, suggesting this species is less tolerant of freshwater than *Fallacia* and *Proschkinia* which increased in abundance upstream.

A range of diatom species were found among the filamentous green and blue-green macroalgae on the walls. These are able to grow despite the vertical plane because silt collects on the macroalgae.

some examples of algae in the Creek

macroalgae

Enteromorpha intestinalis. A green seaweed with long, unbranched tubular fronds which develop from a very small disc holdfast but frequently become detached and form free-floating masses. The plants begin to grow in early spring and die out in autumn when you may find the bleached, dead fronds on the beach. It tends to inhabit older, weathered and porous surfaces. It is used as food in the Far East though not, as far as we know, in Britain. **Rhizoclonium tortuosum**. A filamentous species widespread throughout the Creek. It forms mats of growth at all levels and on foreshore stones.

The other species found were:
Blidingia minima
Blidingia marginata
Enteromorpha prolifera
Pseudendoclonium submarinium
Ulvaria oxysperma
Urospora penicilliformis
Vaucheria sp.
Ectocarpus sp.
Schizothrix arenaria

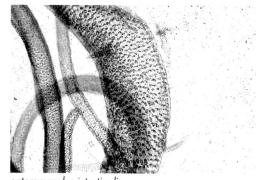

enteromorpha intestinalis

microalgae
The occurrence of *Melosira dubia* is the first recent record of this species in the British Isles. Although it has been recorded occasionally in Europe it is not on the British checklist of species. It may be quite widespread but overlooked.

Hydrosera triquetra is a relatively recent introduction to the UK, previously reported from warmer waters and is thought to show the warming of the Thames from pollution. It must have been carried to the area on ships' hulls from the tropics.

further monitoring

Algal studies are important in assessing water quality and river health. Diatoms are particularly valuable in this respect. Monitoring will contribute to understanding of the ecosystem's functioning and its health.

Quantitative sampling is essential for identifying seasonal variation so macroalgae should be sampled using the belt transect rather than the line transect method used by this survey. Artificial surfaces such as plastic petri-dishes placed in the Creek could be useful for recording the more delicate microalgae which are damaged when surfaces are scraped.

Further searching may reveal the red macroalgae *Audouinella purpurea* in shaded areas and *Porphyridium purpureum* in summer.

impacts of development

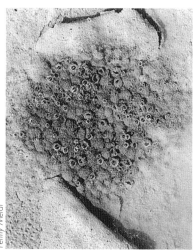

algae growing underwater

Algae make an important contribution to the ecosystem of the tidal Creek. The relatively low diversity of macroalgae could be further reduced if the walls are repaired with non-porous materials. This will also effect those diatoms which flourish in the silt collecting around the macroalgae.

Any change to the tidal nature of the Creek, such as a barrage, would have a devastating effect on the algae, as would dredging.

However, the diversity of algal colonisation could be improved substantially through sympathetic river wall works including porous materials like wood and brick.

mosses and lichens

Mosses and lichens have yet to be surveyed in any detail but the importance of the Creek to these groups became apparent during the flora survey. Moss and lichen communities occur within and above the intertidal range, growing on wood, concrete and brick. They are found on vertical surfaces, particularly aging concrete and other old walls, and on horizontal surfaces, especially wood.

The most surprising species discovered in the Creek is a dog lichen, *Peltigera spuria*, growing on a decaying timber ledge attached to the Creek wall at Gordino's. Dog lichens are rarely seen in the London area; its occurrence here is possibly due to the lack of trampling and the high humidity. It usually grows on well-drained soil or sand. Dog lichens get their name from the supposed similarity of the root-like structures on the under surface of the lichen to a dog's teeth, which is possibly why they were used in the past as a treatment for rabies. Growing with the *Peltigera spuria* is *Cladonia fimbriata*, a more common species in London. Both species were identified by Paddy Coker of the University of Greenwich.

The most common species on the Creek walls, particularly those made of concrete, is *Physcia orbicularis* which is tolerant of some inundation and grows below high water mark. The occasional sunburst of *Xanthoria parietina* can be seen growing in similar places, but usually above high water mark.

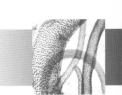

Deptford Power Station Landing Stage has scarcely been used for years this has allowed lichen and moss communities to develop on the timber decking. These include *Lecanora conizaeoides, Lecanora dispersa* and *Candelariella aurella* lichens and *Tortula* and *Bryum* species of moss. Well-developed, extensive colonies like these are rare in the area. Fortunately, unlike the communities growing on the river walls, these can be moved when restoration of the Landing Stage takes place, as long as a location can be found on the river wall where they can be placed in a similar horizontal position protected from excessive shade or trampling.

lichens

Lichens are a curious group of organisms. They are not a single entity but are made up of two unrelated organisms – a fungus and an alga – in a mutually beneficial relationship. The fungal element protects the alga from drying out, thus enabling it to grow. The fungus could not survive without the nutrients generated by algal photosynthesis which it extracts. In all a bizarre but completely successful relationship.

Lecanora conizaeoides mimicking squashed bubblegum

mosses

Mosses are rootless and fancy free. They differ from flowers and most other plants in that they do not have a vascular system to transport water and nutrients through their bodies. They absorb moisture through their leaves. Even less is known about mosses in the Creek than about the lichens.

flora

Prior to the survey commissioned from **Conservation Works** by the Creek Environment Project, data was sparse. Although a number of surveys had taken place previously these only listed a handful of species noted whilst looking over a wall.

techniques

Surveying the Creek is time-consuming and fraught with difficulties. When surveying by boat you are in a constantly moving environment, dependent on the tide and the wind. It proved next to impossible to survey alone. With the assistance of another person the boat can be held relatively still. The confines of the boat mean you cannot step back for an overview but must chose between a close up or a view away from the walls: to change position involves starting up the boat and manoeuvring it.

A further difficulty is that part of the vegetation is always invisible. At high tide part of the vegetation is submerged. At low tide the flora higher up the wall is unreachable and the surfaces of ledges are hidden.

Then there is the impact of the environment on the boat. Detritus, such as plastic bags and the thread from carpets as they break up, constantly snarls the propeller. There is much for the land-lubber to learn: such as keeping the motor away from the wall when starting

identifying plants under the microscope

up. Many rubbing posts have rotted off to below high water mark and others are leaning away at an angle from the wall. Both are invisible at high tide, a hazard to any propeller. On top of this you cannot just wait for a reasonable day to go out and survey; it has to be planned, the tides checked and use of a boat arranged. These frustrations are part of the challenge of getting to know the Creek, a rare and special place, well worth the effort to overcome all obstacles.

Originally the survey was carried out in three reaches separated by bridges: upper, middle and lower, recording separately both sides of the Creek, plus the Theatre Arm and the Transco inlet, a total of nine compartments. In the winter of 96/97 it became clear that this system was inadequate for monitoring events that are about to unfold. Many of the walls in the middle Creek are in need of repair or replacement to maintain flood defences. Two major development sites either side of the lower Creek will have a major impact on the sea walls in that area. Consequently the survey was modified. In the 1997 field season the compartments were allocated by wall type. This considerably increased the number of compartments to 85 and consequently the amount of surveying required. The Thames frontages of the two Greenwich Reach development sites were added.

This change highlighted just how varied the Creek walls are. Each wall has been recorded at least twice at different times of the year. Most have been visited more often. This has been augmented by walking down the upper and middle Creek at low tide (the lower Creek is not accessible on foot), using binoculars where necessary.

The Creek walls have been graded, 0 to 3, according to their species diversity, species rarity, amount of vegetation cover and the vegetation structure. A wall scoring zero would have no or very few plants growing on it. To score 3 a wall would have to have at least two of these qualities to a high degree, for instance; high species diversity covering a large proportion of the available area; or reasonable diversity of plants, reasonable cover and a more structurally diverse vegetation including, for instance, a band of mature buddleja. This is a subjective system, but consistently so.

a wall scoring 3

findings
a unique set of constraints

The Creek walls are of a variety of substrates: wood, concrete, metal, and brick and mortar. These materials have been used at different times and in widely differing manners, creating a visually interesting mix and a range of opportunities for plants to exploit. In general the most diverse walls, in terms of the flora, are made of either brick or wood, although there are exceptions.

The opportunities for colonisation are limited to nooks and crannies, cracks in concrete and wood, gaps between wood, steel or concrete planks, the rotten tops of fenders, ledges of wood or concrete, inundated or not. These nature has exploited to the full.

Seeds will nestle in any cavity they can, although this often causes problems to the mature plant. In many cases the entrance to the cavity is extremely small. The roots penetrate and spread, gathering nutrients to produce a vigorous plant. With this rooting system as support a plant can grow large, but the narrow constriction or bottleneck between roots and stem makes an extremely weak point. The combined effects of gravity and the tide can often break the plant. Occasional high winds can cause localised devastation. Even the light touch of a surveyor can break the fragile hold of garden angelica or hemlock water-dropwort. In decaying timbers the roots expand forcing apart the wood which eventually falls away. On ledges the sheer weight of plants can cause them to break away.

The essential problem for the vegetation is that it is exploiting a finite resource. In most cases it cannot get through to soil behind the sea walls. Most trees are short-lived or they become naturally bonsaied or die back to regrow from the base. So the plants are unwittingly instrumental in the destruction of their own habitat. This highlights the importance of creating new habitat for plants to colonise.

Plants growing lower down the walls are severely affected by the tides. The silt-laden North Sea penetrates the Creek at high tide, leaving a layer of silt on the leaves that dries to a grey colour, affecting the photosynthetic ability of the plant. As an extra burden, they are only able to photosynthesise when the tide is out. The plants worst affected are those that are covered by every tide, those growing in the mud and those growing low down on the walls. Few species are able to tolerate this level of inundation.

the flora of the Creek

The Creek flora is typically urban and characteristic of London. It includes a mixture of native species and a range of species from around the world that make this area locally distinct. The flora is surprisingly diverse, considering that it is growing on sheer walls with the occasional ledge. More than 130 species have been recorded within Deptford Creek. All but one of these species have colonised naturally. Except for some vegetation on the mudflats in the upper Creek, all these species occur on walls.

The flora almost defies classification. It includes an intimate mixture of species from wetland, woodland, grassland and wasteland habitats as well as wall specialists. These include a range of exotica which add considerably to the interest of the Creek and make it typically urban rather than rural.

The top five species in the Creek are, in descending order, buddleja (61 walls), pellitory-of-the-wall (57), hemlock water-dropwort (51), garden angelica (48) and ivy-leaved toadflax (41). These are the classic plants of the Creek that give it much of its character. Studded among these are many species represented by a single specimen. This reflects the scarcity of available habitat for many species, the lack of nearby habitats from which seeds or other plant material might colonise and the low likelihood of it chancing to arrive in an appropriate place to become established.

wetland flora

Of the wetland element of the Creek flora, only garden angelica and Italian alder are not native. Hemlock water-dropwort, celery-leaved buttercup, gipsywort, marsh yellow-cress, pendulous sedge, alder, reed canary-grass, water mint and water figwort all occur, the last three only as single plants in the Creek. Curiously several of the common wetland species are found high and dry on the walls and sometimes behind them. These are garden angelica, hemlock water-dropwort and gipsywort. Common water-starwort and brooklime only occur on the mudflats.

trees and shrubs

Most of the trees and shrubs found in the Creek are non-native. Nine of the 21 species represented only occur as a single specimen. The most common tree is alder, followed by sycamore and ash. Other species are rarer and include silver birch, rowan, Norway maple, Turkey oak, holm oak, leyland cypress and a wild fig tree. Buddleja is by far the most numerous and important shrub on the Creek, providing nesting sites, cover and food for birds. The remaining species are much rarer. They are garden privet, Japanese rose, goat willow, elder, Spanish broom, blackberry and bittersweet.

wasteland flora

A wide range of exotica add to the colour, diversity and distinctiveness of the Creek. Buddleja from China, garden angelica from north and eastern Europe and ivy-leaved toadflax from central and southern Europe are the most prolific. Also found are Michaelmas daisy from North America, beaked hawk's-beard from Europe, Oxford ragwort from southern Europe, along with mind-your-own-business, hollyhock, Japanese rose, Guernsey fleabane from South America, and Canadian fleabane.

characteristic wall species

Four of these species are common in the Creek: ivy-leaved toadflax, pellitory-of-the-wall, Oxford ragwort and buddleja. Others include hart's-tongue fern, red valerian, and wall speedwell.

Nick Bertrand

common polypody fern growing on Mumford's Mill

ferns

Only three species of fern have been recorded in the Creek – bracken, male fern and hart's-tongue fern – and none of them are prevalent. These species are the most common ferns in London and their occurrence here is no great surprise. More of a surprise is that no other species occur. The condition and age of some of the walls would seem ideal for other ferns that occur in the nearby area including the wall specialists wall rue, maidenhair spleenwort and rustyback. Common polypody is hardly representative of the Creek's flora, it is an exceedingly rare fern in London, but it has been found growing in two locations at the top of Mumford's Flour Mill.

saltmarsh species

There are only two species in the Creek which reflect the saline influence of the North Sea. These are sea aster and sea beet. Each is represented by only one plant and both occur on the same wall. This is in the lower Creek and unfortunately is one of the walls to be replaced on the Fairview New Homes site. Both of these species are near their western limit on the Thames here. The river becomes increasingly less saline up river of the Creek. Encroachment into the river has destroyed much of their habitat down river. Just outside the Creek on the beach at Dreadnought Wharf a single specimen of English scurvy-grass at its westernmost limit on the Thames has been discovered.

introductions

The inaccessibility of the Creek means there has been little opportunity for people to plant species on the walls. The only species known to have been planted is a stonecrop by one of the moored barges. Some planting was done in window boxes in the Theatre Arm but these were removed by the DLR contractors, Mowlem, when they moved on site.

mudflats

Shopping trolleys from various supermarkets have escaped into the wild. They are of various subspecies: Booker's, Kwiksave, Sainsbury's Savacentre, Tesco and Co-op. Their impact on the ecology of the Creek has, in one sense, been positive. They have provided obstacles within the channel which have assisted the development of mudflats and hence vegetation. They also provide niches which are exploited by fish fry and invertebrates. The real problem is the human perception of the aesthetics of this kind of 'rubbish' but then the human perception of the Creek and the reality of it bear little relation to each other.

Nickalas Bartrend

absent friends

It is surprising that skullcap does not occur here at all although it does occur on walls of the Thames. Japanese knotweed is notable by its absence although it is commonly seen floating down the Creek and on mudflats at low tide. It is common on the Ravensbourne at and above Lewisham College.

mudflats in the upper Creek

how are the walls colonised?

Seeds arrive from a variety of sources. Water, wind and birds are the main agents of seed dispersal at work here. Garden angelica, hemlock water-dropwort, gipsywort, water figwort and celery-leaved buttercup all have water-borne seeds that drift up and down river on the tides. Curiously the first three of these species are growing high and dry on top of the Creek wall and sometimes behind it. The many composites that occur including dandelion, perennial sow-thistle, hawkweed ox-tongue, Michaelmas daisy, Oxford ragwort, groundsel and cat's ear, are all wind-blown, as are many other species such as silver birch, willowherb and hart's-tongue. Some species such as rowan, ivy, Prunus species and garden privet have probably been sown by birds which eat their berries. How a Turkey oak acorn arrived and then grew on a ledge by the Creek is open to conjecture. Even more so a holm oak seedling that has become established on top of a rubbing post at Sentinel's.

some examples of flowers in the Creek

Ivy-leaved toadflax *Cymbalaria muralis*. Rodney Burton mentions in the *Flora of the London Area* that it was probably first introduced to Stubbers in Havering in 1602 and by 1762 it was frequent on old walls throughout London. It is now common on old walls across the British Isles. In Deptford Creek it is even colonising younger walls, perhaps because of the higher humidity in the Creek. In the surrounding area it is not common and is largely restricted to the old walls of St Paul's and St Nicholas' churchyards. It is occasionally found on clinker or crushed rubble on wasteland sites and railway tracks.

Garden angelica *Angelica archangelica* was formerly cultivated and has now naturalised on river banks in waste places. It occurs as a native species in north and eastern Europe. It is scattered in Britain but has a stronghold in London and is one of the plants that make the Thames locally distinct. It is particularly abundant in Deptford Creek. It is named for its 'angelic' qualities in medicine. It has been regarded as an aphrodisiac, a specific against the plague, an antidote to poisons, and chewing the root apparently provides protection against witches. 'Archangelica' refers to the archangel Raphael who is said to have revealed its virtues. The green stems are candied and used in fruit cakes.

Nick Bertrand

garden angelica growing on a Creek wall

Nick Bertrand

red admiral butterfly feeding on buddleja

Buddleja *Buddleja davidii*. Introduced as a garden plant from China in the 1890s it is now found over the whole of the British Isles except the far north. It is the most abundant woody species on the Creek. It is sometimes called the butterfly-bush because of the high number of butterflies it attracts when in full flower. Holly blue butterfly has been seen by the Creek and it is possible that they are laying eggs on it. There are some moth species that utilise it but we have little information on moths in the Creek. Buddleja has very small, light, winged seeds that spread far and wide and provide a food source for birds such as linnet and goldfinch. In the Creek it is having a variety of positive and negative impacts.

There are some dense thickets which, as well as providing a fast-food outlet for butterflies, offer one of the major nesting habitats for birds in the Creek. Even moorhens are nesting in it where it overhangs the Creek. However, it does shade the wall flora in places and is causing a more rapid decay of the walls than would normally be the case.

Sea aster *Aster tripolium*. This is the only native species of aster. The more familiar Michaelmas daisy *Aster spp.* that are more commonly seen in the wild in London are garden escapes from North America. A marvellous specimen became established in a small hulk on Dreadnought Wharf beach.

sea aster at Dreadnought Wharf

Hemlock water-dropwort *Oenanthe crocata*. Also known as dead tongue, five-fingered rat and horsebane, it is extremely poisonous. Death may occur rapidly or up to eight hours after ingestion: this is one of the most deadly plants in the British Isles. It is frequent on the Creek walls. The Greek 'Oenanthe' means smelling of wine, crocata means saffron-coloured.

further monitoring

During the period of the survey the dynamics of the vegetation have begun to be revealed. There is much more to be found out. Detailed mapping of the wall flora will allow a greater appreciation of the Creek's diversity. The education centre will enable students to carry out some of this research.

Ledges are an important feature of the Creek. Many were constructed during the 1960s and 70s, before the Thames Barrier was built, when a programme of interim defence raising was carried out to all the Thames tidal defences. This work usually comprised a short wall about 600mm high built on top of the existing defences. These were often set back a little, leaving a ledge on the river-side of the wall. Other ledges occur lower down on the walls. Further work on recording which plants colonise ledges at exactly what levels is needed to discover the optimum range of heights to install new ledges.

impacts of development

All of the recent works to the Creek walls are hostile to nature. Not only are they inhospitable they are totally out of character with the rest of the Creek walls. The two major eyesores are the Lewisham Waste Transfer Station where the walls are sheet steel piles and devoid of plant life, and the Lewisham College site, which is mostly of engineering brick construction but does support a few plants.

The greatest threat, a barrage across the Creek, has, at least for the moment, been kicked into touch. The proposals for the river walls that have to be repaired or replaced have been subject to much discussion and will be far better than anything that has happened in the Creek to date. The greatest loss that is taking place and which is likely to continue is of terrestrial habitat adjacent to the Creek.

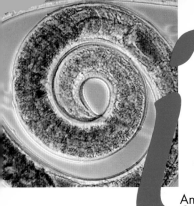

*i*nvertebrates

Animals without backbones are known as invertebrates. The Creek is an exceptionally important refuge for many of these organisms and supports familiar groups, such as insects, worms and molluscs, as well as several less widely known groups, such as nematodes, copepods and mites.

aquatic invertebrates

Within a comparatively condensed stretch, the Creek offers a unique combination of wet and fully aquatic habitats that are exposed to different regimes of fresh and salty (brackish) water. This, along with the almost infinite variety of substrates (mixtures of mud, sand, gravel, stones and wood), is the key to the Creek's success in supporting large numbers of aquatic invertebrates. Scientific surveys have confirmed that the Creek is a valuable reservoir of aquatic invertebrates and that the biodiversity of the watercourse is high.

techniques

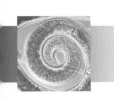

Unicomarine were contracted by the Environment Agency to survey the invertebrates in the central channel, the intertidal region and the walls in May 1997. The **University of Greenwich** also surveyed the distribution and abundance of aquatic macroinvertebrates (those which can be seen without magnification). This survey, undertaken in summer 1996 and winter 1996-97 was also designed to expand current knowledge of the influence of water salinity and seasonality on invertebrates in the Creek. More recently **Physalia Ltd** were commissioned by the Creek Environment Project to investigate invertebrate communities in the proposed area of the Floating Education Centre.

core sampling in the Creek

Physalia Ltd

Several different techniques have been used to examine and describe the communities of invertebrates present in each of the Creek's different habitats. These included:

- core sampling where muds, sands and gravels were present on the shores. This method examines organisms that live within the sediments.
- transects and quadrats to examine the communities of surface-living animals at different positions on the shores – a common technique for studying the organisms that live on and under larger, more stable stones.
- kick-net sampling to examine the animals on the bed of the main channel that are permanently covered by water.
- scrape sampling used on the walls of the Creek to study the animals associated with the attached communities of algae ('epigrowth').

Except for the largest animals that were released back into the Creek, samples were preserved and examined in laboratories. This enabled the densities of the Creek's invertebrates as well as their diversity to be described. Depending on the groups being examined, different methods were used to study them. The larger invertebrates (macrofauna) were sorted by sieving onto half millimetre mesh sieves. These animals were then identified under low power microscopes. The microscopic invertebrates that live between sediment particles (meiofauna) were washed out of the sediments onto very fine mesh sieves (mesh down to 38 millionths of a metre). These animals were examined under high power microscopes at magnifications up to 1,000x.

findings

The scientific studies of the Creek have identified over 50 aquatic invertebrates. These include species that have not been recorded in the Thames estuary or its creeks before and, in the case of the meiofauna, a species that is possibly new to science.

the main channel

The bed of the channel is home to a comparatively broad range of fresh and brackish water animals. At low tides, the distribution of these species along the Creek depends on the salinity ('saltiness') of the water. This, in turn, is determined by the tidal fall and the freshwater flow from the rivers. Another important factor is the presence of hard substrata that develop a surface layer of algae and micro-organisms (bacteria, fungi and protozoa). This nutritious layer is food for several species that browse on the growth using rasping or scraping mouthparts. Examples include the snail *Potamopyrgus jenkinsii* and the limpet *Ancylus fluviatilis*. The brackish water amphipod shrimp *Gammarus zaddachi* is the most abundant organism in

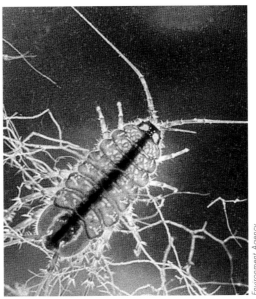
Environment Agency

water hoglouse

the watercourse and, along with water hoglouse *Asellus aquaticus*, feeds on rotting vegetation. Other crustaceans present in the Creek include the estuarine prawn *Palaemon longirostris*, the Chinese mitten crab *Eriocheir sinensis*, and, at the lower end of the Creek, the marine shrimp *Crangon crangon*, that enters estuaries seasonally to breed. Tubifex worms (small relatives of earthworms) are exceptionally abundant where pockets of stabilised mud exist.

the intertidal shores

Among the macrofauna, the mud communities are almost exclusively tubifex and limnodrilus worms. Densities of up to 2 million per square metre have been recorded adjacent to the site of the Ha'penny Hatch bridge (late July 1998). The microscopic meiofauna are more abundant and more diverse – over 3.3 million nematodes (free-living roundworms) were recorded per square metre at the bridge. A single 120 ml mud sample contained over 6,000 meiofauna of 18 different species.

In contrast to the muds, the macrofauna on the stone-mud shores are more diverse and include browsing snails, amphipod shrimps, insect larvae (midges) and nests of leeches with their egg cocoons attached to the undersides of stones. The leeches may feed on the worms and the amphipod shrimps.

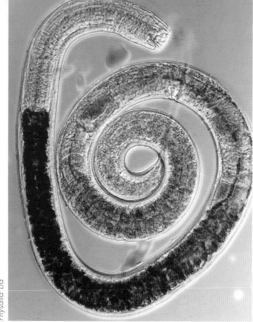

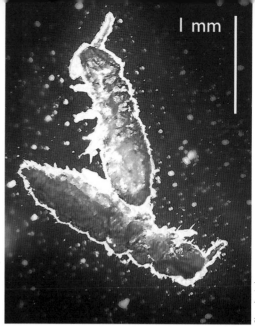

1 mm

a predatory nematode

Hypogastrura viatica – a new record for the Thames

the creek walls

In contrast to steel and concrete, wherever wood is present on the Creek walls, rich algal communities develop on the wetted surfaces. This epigrowth traps sediments and supports several invertebrates including insects. Springtails *Colembolla* are small, primitive insects that feed on organic materials. In 1998, a new record for the Thames estuary was found in the Deptford Creek wall communities *Hypogastrura viatica*. Midge larvae *Chironomidae* are also present in the algae and the weak-flying adults that they become are an important component of the diet of the Creek's black redstarts.

some aquatic invertebrates

macrofauna

Freshwater shrimps. Amphipod shrimps *Gammarus zaddachi* are the dominant crustaceans. These are not true shrimps but are relatives of the 'sand-hoppers' that live among seaweed on beaches. Since they feed on decomposing plant material transported into the Creek from the rivers, the shrimps are most common where the bed is a mixture of stones and mud. These substrates trap their food and provide protection from predators (fish and birds) as well as shelter when they are caught on the shores on falling tides. When the tide is in, comparatively large 'herds' of the shrimps migrate up and down, browsing as they go.

Estuarine prawns. Larger than the freshwater shrimps, the prawn *Palaemon longirostris* is usually present in sub-tidal sites in moderately low numbers. It is distinguished from the true shrimp by a sharp spike (rostrum) on the front of its head. This crustacean is particularly mobile and scavenges on the remains of dead animals as well as feeding on detritus. The prawns avoid predators by means of rapid tail flips that propel them backward through the water. This often causes them to jump out of sampling nets.

Tubifex worms. The muddy sediments are characterised by high densities of tubifex worms and their relatives. These small animals are related to the common earthworm and their densities can reach up to 19 million per square metre. Most of the species have a specialised blood pigment that allows them to live in oxygen-poor habitats such as mud. They feed by eating sediments that are rich in bacteria and decaying plant material. In the River Lea these worms are collected as food for tropical fish.

Chinese mitten crabs. So called because of the masses of fine filaments present around the claws, the Chinese mitten crab *Eriocheir sinensis* is an species introduced from the rivers of China. They can live in both marine and freshwater habitats. Each year the adults migrate down to the sea to breed and release their young before beginning the long return journey back to the rivers. The crabs are often classed as pests as they burrow into riverbanks causing considerable damage.

Chinese mitten crab

meiofauna

Nematodes. In the Creek, these microscopic, free-living roundworms include plant-parasitic species, bacterial feeders, deposit feeders, predators, diatom feeders, epigrowth feeders and omnivores. All the species are characteristic of low salinity water and one, a *Pareudiplogaster*, is believed to be new to science. Several particularly sensitive nematode groups are present and this indicates that the sediments are not heavily contaminated.

Copepods. In the Creek sediments, these shrimp-like animals are predominantly surface-dwelling (epibenthic) creatures. The comparatively large, mobile species present are characteristic of estuarine muds and feed on the fine, particulate organic matter transported in from the freshwater catchment. Copepods form an important food source for juvenile flounders.

further studies and monitoring

The ease of access that will be afforded by the new Education Centre will enable several important studies to be undertaken on the Creek's aquatic invertebrate communities. New ecological information can be obtained on an enormous variety of topics including the migrations of the Chinese mitten crabs, the seasonal variations in the populations of the freshwater shrimps and the interactions between predators and their prey. The Creek will also provide an important site for the study of impacts of developments on estuarine invertebrate communities. This will benefit planners and regulators throughout the country as it will enable the adverse effects of developments on aquatic communities to be identified and effective mitigation and management techniques to be investigated.

impacts of development

The Creek is a valuable ecosystem because of the variety of mixed substrates that are exposed to the daily cycles of tides and salinity changes. Superimposed over a comparatively short distance, these environmental features sustain the high biodiversity of the Creek invertebrate assemblages. Any development that removes primary habitat (mud, sand, gravel and stones) or changes the nature of these substrates and the salinity regimes within the Creek, will directly affect the communities of invertebrates. Although less obvious, simple shading of the Creek sediments and walls will also have an adverse effect on the algal communities. The algae are essential as either food or shelter for many of the invertebrates described above and their loss will have immediate effects on the invertebrate populations.

terrestrial invertebrates

Terrestrial invertebrates offer some of the best models for ecological study. They are numerous, diverse and relatively well known. They usually occur within particular habitats and are often associated with specific plants or specific ecological niches (microhabitats). They form a major part in many food chains.

Terrestrial invertebrates are important in the assessment of any habitat because whatever the habitat, there are species linked to it – species which indicate the quality of a site, its ecological diversity (complexity), its age, its very nature and character. Many are indicators of cleanliness or pollution; others show the degree of natural continuity or disturbance by human interference.

techniques

An initial terrestrial invertebrate survey was carried out by **Richard Jones** in September, October and November 1997. This was followed up during spring and summer 1998. Nine sections of the Creek walls were identified as being under threat of development. These were visited by boat at high tide and on foot at low tide. Insects and other invertebrates were sought by whatever means possible in the challenging circumstances – the sites to be surveyed were, after all, effectively vertical walls.

Handfuls of soil, leaf litter, rotten wood and algae slime were snatched from the walls and sieved into a plastic tray in the boat. Rotten timber piles were gently prised apart to reveal their inhabitants. Crevices were examined by torchlight and spiders sucked out using a 'pooter'. Plants and flowers were searched for visiting insects, surfaces were examined for resting and sheltering individuals, and specimens were captured by hand or with an insect net.

'pootering' for invertebrates

At low tide, some piles were examined using a ladder from the Creek bed, and stones and rubbish were turned over. On visits to the tops of the walls, small pockets of soil and leaf litter were finger-tip searched or sieved, and the herbage was deftly attacked with a sweep net.

findings

During the initial autumn and winter survey, only 92 species of terrestrial invertebrates were found, mostly beetles, bugs, woodlice and spiders, hibernating in the nooks and crannies or sheltering in the sparse clumps of herbage. But during the follow-up, carried out in spring and summer 1998, the lush growth of leaves and flowers attracted a much wider selection of insects including all those flying creatures like bees, wasps, hoverflies, butterflies and moths which were absent during the cold and wet.

The main outcome of the survey was to show that an essentially mundane artificial habitat had been successfully colonised by a broad variety of invertebrate types. Whilst most species were quite common and widespread, several were unusual or even rare. Rich communities of invertebrate life were found in the old timber and crumbling walls of the Creek. These insects, spiders and other 'creepy-crawlies' play a major part in the Creek ecosystem. They contribute to the diets of birds and fish (and each other); they break down and recycle the nutrients from rotten wood, leaf litter and other decaying organic material; they pollinate flowers and generally enliven the Creek's perceived bleak urban landscape. It is heartening to discover that what, at first sight, appears to be an unprepossessing place, a series of derelict commercial wharfs, crumbling, rotten and bedraggled, is far from dead. It is teeming with life!

some terrestrial invertebrates

remarkable diversity

Even during the most miserable part of the year, during the initial autumn and winter survey period, it soon became clear that the invertebrates of Deptford Creek were not just those run-of-the-mill species expected to turn up in any derelict plot of wasteland. There was remarkable diversity and there were several species regarded as being nationally scarce. As the spring and summer follow-up progressed, even more unusual creatures started to turn up.

A small **weevil** *Kalcapion semivittatum* was found feeding on its host-plant annual mercury on disturbed soil above one of the wharves. It is more or less confined to the London basin and a few other sites in south east England and is regarged as being nationally scarce ('notable status A') because it is known from less than 30 localities in the UK.

One of Britain's most uncommon **ladybirds** turned up in May and June 1998. The Adonis ladybird *Adonia variegata* is like a very small and narrow version of the common 7-spot ladybird, although the spot patterns vary tremendously from 3 to 15 small black marks on the red background. It is nationally scarce ('notable status B') because it is known from between 31 and 100 UK localities. Although found in a number of habitats from gardens to heathland, it appears to be predominantly a coastal species and is fairly widely distributed in London and the Thames estuary.

Richard A. Jones

Adonia variegata

Several butterflies were seen during the spring of 1998, including the **comma** *Polygonia c-album* and **red admiral** *Vanessa atalanta*. The comma has a remarkable history in England in that it declined dramatically from being very common and widespread in the 1850s to almost absent by 1910. At the very bottom of its fortunes in about 1913 it was more or less confined to the English-Welsh borders. This sudden disappearance has been attributed to a decline in the farming of hops, the butterfly's main foodplant. But by the 1930s the comma was on the move again across England; in the 1950s it was all over the London area and it remains today one of our most common species. Why the sudden increase? A change of caterpillar foodplant from hops to stinging nettles has allowed this beautiful butterfly to regain its old geographic spread and it is now more widespread than at any other time in its known history. How ironic, then, that in Deptford Creek it is breeding on the hop plants which overhang the flood defence walls cascading down into the water where once barge loads of dried hops from the fields of Kent were shipped to the breweries of London.

The prettily marked **orb web spider**
Larionodes sclopetaria was common along
many parts of the Creek walls. It is a
widespread but nevertheless very local
spider, one particularly associated with
bridges, fences and walls near water,
especially those along rivers and canals.

Very many specimens of a minute **millipede**
Polyxenus lagurus were found in soil and leaf
litter on some of the most exposed ledges
just above the high water mark along many
parts of the Creek. It is a peculiar creature
which lives in small colonies, feeding on
decaying plant material in two disparate
habitats – ancient broad-leaved woodlands
and exposed rocky coastlines.

There was one very uncommon species,
Olibrus flavicornis, a **flower beetle** which
has 'Red Data Book' status because it is so
seldom encountered. It is thought to breed in
the flower heads of hawkweed ox-tongue
and it occurred in several places in the Creek.
Nationally it is very rare and is known only
from a handful of coastal and estuarine
grassland sites in south east England.

orb web spider (Larionodes sclopetaria)

polyxenus lagurus

sun-traps

One unexpected feature of the Creek is only revealed on warm sunny days, when certain
areas along the tops of the river walls become blisteringly hot. South-facing buildings close
to the Creek create sheltered sun-traps where warmth-loving insects like bees and wasps
are encouraged to forage and nest. Several mason wasps make their nests in crumbling
walls and timber on the Creek including one, *Microdynerus exilis*, which is nationally scarce
('notable status B') and usually associated with chalk downland, heathland edges, gravel
pits and sunny woodlands.

Spider-hunting wasps are a characteristic group of heat-loving insects which hunt across
short turf and patches of bare ground after the crab- and wolf-spiders with which they
provision their nests. To find one on Deptford Creek was a great surprise, particularly when
it turned out to be a nationally scarce ('notable status B') species, *Auplopus carbonarius*,
associated with broad-leaved woodland.

origin of the invertebrate fauna

One of the important aims of any invertebrate survey is to try to understand how
invertebrate communities have become established and how they have developed. Already
there are clues as to how insects get into the Creek. One day in June 1998, whilst surveying
in the upper reaches near Lewisham College, two very curious finds served to illustrate the
importance of wind and water as the prime agents of insect dispersal in the area.

A stag beetle *Lucanus cervus* crawling up the wall a few inches above the incoming tide
could only have flown there from a suburban garden somewhere in the area where it spent
several years as a grub feeding in an old tree stump. There is certainly no suitable habitat
anywhere in the Creek that it could have come from and it must have been brought by the

wind. The towering edifice of Mumford's Mill creates powerful down-draughts when the wind is from the south west and the obvious explanation is that the beetle, flying innocently by, was blown off-course and dumped unceremoniously into the Creek.

A few yards away, a small weevil *Notaris scirpi* was knocked out of a small clump of vegetation into the insect net. It is nationally scarce ('notable status B') and feeds on lesser pond sedge and reedmace. Although both are waterside plants, neither grows in the Creek. However, reedmace does occur further up the Ravensbourne river system and it seems likely that the beetle was washed down from more suitable habitats above.

There is, as always in such urban sites, evidence of human action introducing new species into the Creek ecosystem. In early April 1998, the scruffy and exposed foreshore of Dreadnought Wharf produced *Xiphydria camelus* a large wood-boring sawfly and *Biphylus lunatus* a tiny fungus beetle. The sawfly is a denizen of wet woodlands where it breeds in the dead wood of alder and birch logs and the fungus beetle is regarded as an ancient woodland indicator species which breeds in 'crampballs', a knobbly black fungus of ash, birch and a few other trees. Both these insects are wholly out of place in a tidal river estuary and had apparently come to Deptford Creek in a small dead birch tree dumped on the foreshore with a load of rubble and other detritus. There is no telling what will turn up next.

further monitoring

The Creek is constantly changing. The physical nature of the river walls is changing each year as dereliction and repair compete with each other, and invertebrates continue to come and go. Already other parts of the Creek are being surveyed, those less threatened with development, and the final study will eventually have covered a full year.

It is hoped that some invertebrate surveying will be possible in the future so that any commercial development and new flood defence work on Deptford Creek can be monitored It will be important to see how the invertebrate fauna is affected and how any replacement Creek walls are colonised from scratch.

impacts of development

It had to be assumed that in repairing the river frontages all of the current invertebrate habitats such as rotten timber, broken brickwork and crumbling concrete, would be destroyed and replaced by newly-built flood defence walls. Given this constraint, the survey report argued that designs for the new walls should incorporate features to encourage invertebrate colonisation anew.

Crevices, holes, overhangs and ledges are of great importance to invertebrate life and tiny spaces can house large colonies. Such nooks and crannies should be built into the new walls as they are created, and they should be 'inoculated' with specimens, leaf litter, soil and rotten wood from other parts of the Creek.

The ecology of the Creek today, exemplified by the insects and other invertebrates occurring there, is very clearly based on invasion, recolonisation and adaptation to man-made structures. As major riverside development looms, the designers, planners, engineers and builders intent on their Deptford schemes are faced with two options. They can scour the creekside of all its living material and replace it with dead metal and concrete, or they can take the lead that nature has given and use it to enhance the new flood walls, making Deptford Creek a place of continuing ecological interest and natural beauty.

fish

Deptford Creek is the northern end of the river Ravensbourne which has its source in Keston in Kent. It flows through Bromley, Downham, Catford and Lewisham before it reaches the Thames at Deptford. The total length of the river is 41 miles (66 km). The river catchment area is mostly urban in nature and about 30 km of its course is in culvert (covered over or channelled). Prior to the urban and industrial growth of the 20th century, the Ravensbourne supported substantial freshwater fish populations and brown trout were common in the river downstream of Bromley. Large commercial fisheries for smelt, whitebait (the mixed young of herring and sprat) and shrimp were taken from Greenwich Reach. Many of these were landed at wharves in Deptford Creek. The 20th century brought pollution which killed off most of the fish. Today average water quality in the freshwater Ravensbourne is good enough to support fish life, but due to its urban surroundings, the water in the Ravensbourne is heavily effected by run-off during heavy rain and storms. Often the first flush of surface water from a heavy rainfall can be of poor quality. It can also be so fast-flowing that it washes small fish downstream.

In contrast to the rest of the Ravensbourne, Deptford Creek displays a rich and varied habitat at low water provided by the wealth of debris such as shopping trolleys and old tyres in the low water channel.

The tides and currents in the Thames are strong and can easily overpower young fish. Deptford Creek is used as shelter for a wide variety of fish fry, especially flounder fry and elvers (baby eels). Creeks also provide valuable shelter and refuge for fish from both predation and poor water quality incidents in the main river close by.

common gobies

Physalia Ltd

techniques

The whole of the River Ravensbourne was surveyed by the **National Rivers Authority** in November 1991 and then by its successor, the **Environment Agency**, in July 1996. The earlier survey also drew upon a qualitative study of fish in Deptford Creek undertaken by Liverpool University in July 1991. Surveys were also undertaken on Greenwich beach at high tide in 1992-93. In the summer of 1997 surveyors investigated the Creek at high tide with a net to see what they could pick up.

Each of the studies surveyed one site in the Creek, a length of around 400 metres near the Faircharm trading estate. The low water channel in the centre of the Creek was fished at low water on a neap tide to minimise salinity. Electracatch pulsed DC electric fishing equipment was used to send a low electrical pulse through the water which stuns the fish making them float to the surface. When the counting and identifying is complete the fish can be released, a little shocked but otherwise unharmed.

Fish surveying has its limitations. Electracatch surveying has to be undertaken at low tide for it to be effective but a variety of fish will only use the Creek at high tide. The margins of a mature derelict creek such as Deptford Creek make sampling by any method at high tide very difficult. Visual observations and information from anglers are often the only sources of information. A few fishermen do angle in the Creek occasionally for eels and flounder. Kick sampling is a technique used to catch very small fry, as little as 6mm in length. Seine netting is the technique used on the shore at Greenwich, but this can only be applied for the few minutes around slack water at low tide, when the river temporarily ceases to flow. Many of the fish that use the Creek are seasonal and therefore only present at particular times of year.

findings

Both reports expressed concern that the fish populations recovered were "very poor, with low species diversity and small populations" despite good water quality indicators. However, Deptford Creek was identified on both occasions as a substantial habitat due to the considerable debris. Common gobies were abundant in the lower Creek, three-spined stickleback abundant further upstream near the weirs. The Creek showed a distinctive pattern of eels and flounder.

a flounder caught during a low tide public walk

The 1991 survey caught 52 eels and 42 flounders, along with a single dace and a single roach which were thought to have escaped from a pond further upstream.

The 1996 survey recorded at low tide several hundred eels of between 80mm and 485mm and thousands of flounder of between 20mm and 60mm, as well as two dace. One of the dace was marked and had probably been washed down from a restocking project further up the Ravensbourne at Winsford Road.

some examples of fish in the Creek

Eel. The eel is a migrant fish in the Creek. All eels allegedly originate in the Sargasso Sea. As larvae, the eels take up to three years to float on the Gulf Stream to England. The elvers (baby eels), which are still transparent and are known as glass eels, arrive in English waters in early spring. Within a month of arriving, they have developed pigmentation and look like miniature eels. By mid April they are 65mm long. As they get older they tend to move upstream finding somewhere without many eels and staying. Female eels have a tendency to go much further upstream than the males and grow to enormous sizes. Modern elver migrations or 'elver runs' are not as big as they once were. Two hundred years ago many authors cited the thick black lines of elvers migrating upstream in the spring. These were known as eel fare. Elvers were regarded as an important delicacy. Recolonisation is happening slowly because of the low elver numbers. Even so, today the eel can be found as far upstream as Beckenham.

Common goby. These also migrate up through the estuary in June, as small as 6mm in length, but only stay for the summer and autumn in the estuary as far upstream as Deptford. In the summer months they can be seen in large numbers on the new channel bed at Brookmill Park.

Flounder. The adult flounder is generally a coastal fish and they only tend to penetrate into freshwater as fry. The fry of the flounder and goby are very clever. They can sense when the tide changes direction. They float up in the current on the flooding tide. As soon as the tide turns, they shelter in the margins of the river close to the riverbed. Using this method, called active tidal transport, the baby fish can move distances of 18 miles in one day.

Environment Agency

flounder

future monitoring

The regular five year survey programme will revisit the Ravensbourne catchment and Deptford Creek in 2001. However, the rich variety of wall habitats and other features planned for the regeneration of the Creek are very novel. Special local fish surveys will be conducted from early 2000 to see whether the fish fry actually use the new habitat created. Experience elsewhere shows that this does happen. Such appraisal studies are already being undertaken for some newly-created habitats, such as the tidal terracing created on the Greenwich Millennium Exhibition site for example.

impacts of development

The prime factor identified as constraining the Ravensbourne fisheries was the impoverishment of habitats imposed by past engineering practices. Flood defence had focused on channel widening and straightening, replacing the natural river course with concrete channels. This approach left very little of the river in semi-natural condition. Since 1986 the Thames Water Authority, the National Rivers Authority and the Environment Agency have developed a different approach, with the emphasis on restricting development in the flood plain. This has offered scope for more environmentally sensitive engineering options.

Urban run-off can cause water quality problems. Urban streams tend to be very flashy with a fast discharge of the run-off. Removal of in-stream habitats and channel narrowing, will tend to remove habitat as well as increase flows and therefore increase the potential for fish wash-out.

In tidal creeks, all of the above applies, but the exposed shores at low tide represent the most productive aquatic environments of all. They provide specialised feeding and nursery grounds. Further narrowing by development (known as tidal encroachment), will not only remove habitat but will also tend to increase the flow. This may be sufficient to wash fish out. A continuous foreshore is a vital element in the migration of fish and their fry through the estuary. Narrowing to the point where no foreshore exists could cause the fish fry migrations to cease. Tidal barrages provide more obstructions to migration. A fish pass can be built into a barrage to allow large fish to pass, but tiny fish fry could be denied access to the river upstream completely.

fishy tales

lunchtime eel fishing

There's a friendly cove who goes fishing behind Booker's Cash and Carry in the upper Creek. He fishes for eels using worms as bait. Though he is primarily a sea angler, he enjoys the tranquillity of this hideaway on Deptford Creek to fish during his lunch break or after work. He does not mind whether he catches anything or not and enjoys observing his fellow 'fishermen', the herons, go about their business. To avoid catching his line on the many shopping trolleys or other debris on the Creek bed, he first selects a relatively clear patch of Creek at low tide and removes any remaining obstacles by hand. When he does catch eels he takes them home and cooks them for supper – delicious! Recently he caught two eels, the bigger one he reckoned was a conger eel (a marine species). It had teeth and bit off the head of the other eel while in the kitchen sink awaiting the pot. *(Mike Paice)*

just getting the feel for eels

My kids have always fished down the Stowage. They used to bring home eel. The neighbour round the corner jellies them and gives them out. I've never been that brave though, to eat them. I don't like eel.

My son, Jack, has put eel in Twinkle Park pond. They've been stocking up the pond so they can fish in it. They sit round there with their fishing gear.

"What are you doing?"

"We're just getting the feel of it."

I haven't got any patience for fishing. I'd get bored. My family are right into it. Jack knows if he goes out fishing on his own he has to make sure of the tides. My husband worked on the docks but he is a fisherman as well. The thing people don't understand is that water is only dangerous if you abuse it. *(Bridget Perry)*

a surprising carp

I regularly fished the Thames in my youth from the upper reaches around Oxford to the wider stretches at Hampton Court. I knew of Deptford Creek but assumed there would be no resident fish because the low tides leave too shallow a depth.

I began working on the Creek Environment Project in autumn 1997. On my first low tide walk hundreds of flounder gave away their presence with a cloud of silt when disturbed. Their perfectly camouflaged bodies make them impossible to see until they kick off the bottom to find a safer place to dwell. However, except for the occasional deep hole that I was quick to find, the water was still not deep enough to support populations of larger fish.

A local resident and surveyor told me he had photographed a 'catch' made in the summer months from the middle Creek. The description sounded like a species of carp; but surely carp wouldn't be found in the Creek? After many months the photograph was found. It turned out to be common carp, the largest around 5lbs in weight. In my opinion these fish were only visitors to the Creek, perhaps permanently located around the mouth and coming in to feed or take shelter with the rising tides of the Thames.

the one that didn't get away

I began talking more regularly with the resident boaters. Julian Kingston, who used to moor in the Theatre Arm, said in previous summers the large submerged bodies of fish could be seen venturing up with the tides. He had noted their absence for over a year and wondered what had happened. The disappearance could be due to disturbance from surrounding development, or a temporary increase in the salinity of the Thames pushing the shoal upstream. So much for my local fishery! *(Jon Ducker)*

birds

Over fifty species of birds have been seen on or around Deptford Creek over the last few years, a surprisingly high number for such an urban location. While some of these are casual visitors which have only been seen flying over, more than thirty occur regularly, including the nationally rare black redstart, the stately grey heron and the stunningly beautiful kingfisher. Many of these birds are rarely found anywhere else in the Deptford and Greenwich area. The presence of so many birds, with several charismatic species, makes the Creek an interesting place for birdwatchers and an ideal site for environmental education.

techniques

The Creek was surveyed for birds by **John Archer**, **Dusty Gedge**, **Mike Paice** and **Peter Massini**. The method employed was a standard walk incorporating six five-minute stops. Every month a survey was done at high and low tide. A ten-minute count has also been undertaken at Mumford's Mill at irregular intervals since September 1995. All birds seen or heard were recorded. Stand-ardised recording methods allow for changes in bird populations to be monitored. Observations from local birdwatchers help to fill in any gaps left by the standard surveys. Bird habitats have also been assessed.

Nick Berrand

a leisurely way to look out for birds

findings

Deptford Creek is highly urbanised and its channel has been severely constricted. Bird habitats typical of more natural tidal creeks – such as reed beds, saltmarsh and extensive mudflats – are replaced by harsher but nevertheless interesting habitats. These include open water, narrow strips of intertidal mud, a few bushes growing out of cracks in the walls, and some small (and decreasing) areas of adjacent wasteland habitats.

Habitats for nesting are particularly scarce. There are few horizontal surfaces above the high water mark and little suitable cover nearby. It is therefore not surprising that only four species of birds which are particularly associated with water regularly nest here: mallard, moorhen, grey wagtail and pied wagtail. The intertidal mud provides valuable feeding habitat for a much wider variety of birds and a dozen or so additional species of waterbirds frequently feed in the Creek. The most important areas for these are the mud banks near the Creek mouth, which are favoured by several species of ducks, gulls and waders, and the rubbish-strewn area in front of Lewisham College, where shopping trolleys provide cover for secretive birds such as moorhens. In all, 23 species of aquatic or waterside birds have been recorded during the last three years. A further 30 species of birds recorded during the surveys are essentially land birds which utilise the habitats around the Creek. About 20 of these, including black redstart and linnet (both species of national conservation concern), probably breed in the area or are frequent visitors, while the others are occasional migrants passing through.

some examples of birds around the Creek

A few species which are typical of the Creek or of particular significance are briefly discussed below.

Bill Varney

grey wagtail

Grey wagtail. Usually considered as a bird of fast-flowing streams, the grey wagtail has become more frequent as a breeding bird in London in recent years. Three or four pairs now nest beside Deptford Creek, usually in crevices in the Creek walls. They can be seen throughout the year. The area in front of Lewisham College is a favourite foraging area, where the trolleys and other rubbish mimic the rocks of the grey wagtail's more usual mountain streams.

Kingfisher. The abundant small fish in the Creek attract this beautiful, iridescent blue and orange bird. Kingfishers can be seen in the Creek throughout the year, and probably breed further upstream on the River Ravensbourne. They may perhaps be persuaded to nest in the Creek if a suitable steep sandy bank could be provided. They can sometimes be seen perched on a shopping trolley, waiting for a passing fish, but a more common encounter is a piercing whistle followed by a flash of cobalt blue.

Cormorant. The cormorant is traditionally considered to be a sea bird and has an almost prehistoric appearance. The species has become established as a resident in London since 1990 and there are now nearly 200 breeding pairs. Locally, it is most frequently encountered in the lower Creek area, particularly around the Power Station Landing Stage. They can be seen diving for eels and, after feeding, they are occasionally seen, wings outstretched, drying themselves in the sun.

Marie O'Connell

cormorant on a perch in the Creek

Mike Paice

kestrel

Kestrel. Britain's commonest birds of prey, a pair of kestrels has successfully nested in Mumford's Mill for at least the last three years, and is nesting again in 1998. While kestrels in the countryside feed largely on small mammals, those in urban areas eat a greater proportion of birds, particularly sparrows and starlings. Interestingly, the Mumford's pair have also been seen to take feral pigeons, a much larger prey than is usual for this small falcon.

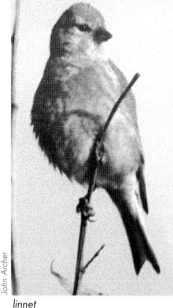

John Archer

linnet

Linnet. This delightful finch breeds around the lower areas of the Creek on wasteland and industrial plots. This species is on the Red List of breeding birds. Birds on this list are of greatest concern and deserve urgent and effective conservation action. Over the last 25 years the population has crashed by 50% so the Creek is very lucky to have them. They can more often than not be seen flying over the Creek Road bridge or singing from the top of a buddleja bush. The birds nest and feed on these bushes. The wasteland flora of the Creek walls and industrial plots also provide the seeds they need to feed on. In 1997 at least eight pairs bred, though more probably bred on the Deptford Power Station site which is now sadly lost to housing development.

Grey heron. This elegant bird can often be seen on the Creek at low tide as it slowly stalks the water's edge for fish. Even at night it can seen fishing under the street lights at the Creek Road bridge and Lewisham College. In 1996 a total of 12 birds used to roost on the Deptford Power Station site. Since the development of this site the numbers have dropped but two or three can often be seen at high tide on the jetty and on the yellow buoys in the Thames.

Mute swan. A regular visitor to the Creek, the royal mute swan did in fact attempt to breed on the Creek in 1997. The nest, on a pallet next to the Bird's Nest public house, was unfortunately covered over with mud by Mowlem, the DLR contractors. The pair tried again on the mud bank opposite Lewisham College. A series of high tides soon washed the nest and eggs away. It is believed that this pair may have been displaced from the Brookmill Park pond when development started there and it is hoped they will return on completion of the works. Although it would be good to see the birds breed on the

Marie O'Connell

swanning around on the Creek

Creek, some experts have suggested that the muddy nature of the Creek could cause cygnets to get stuck and thus engulfed by incoming tides.

impacts of development

As the Creek has been neglected for so long, bird species have been able to inhabit the area without the threat of disturbance. The loss of wasteland habitats will make it less likely to hold breeding black redstarts unless novel approaches to landscaping are implemented. Any insistence by riparian owners on sheet metal flood defences will also have a negative impact on this species, along with grey wagtails. The other major impact will be the increased access along the lower Creek. Wintering wildfowl will not tolerate high human access around this area of the Creek. Responsible access would be preferable, allowing people to view the Creek at certain points but leaving areas of 'quiet' so that birds can feed and rest up without disturbance. Planners and developers need to understand that this is a wildlife habitat which development per se does not have to eradicate but could in fact enhance. It remains to be seen whether those in the planning departments can take up this challenge and make the Creek a better place for both its human users and its wildlife.

black redstarts

This is a nationally rare bird, protected under Schedule 1 of the Wildlife and Countryside Act 1981. The national population is less than 100 pairs; 7% are found along Deptford Creek. The bird is typical of urban wastelands and large industrial sites where derelict or undisturbed buildings and sparse

female black redstart

vegetation resemble its more natural mountain habitat. The species has adapted to a life linked to human activity. In Germany, where it is quite common, it is known as the house redstart. Britain is the limit of its range and it has only been breeding here since 1923. During and after the war it was famous for breeding on bomb sites. As these were re-developed the birds moved eastwards to industrial land and wasteland along the docks.

The kinds of places black redstarts breed are rarely visited by birdwatchers so the species is very often overlooked. The commissioning of the surveys has drawn attention to their presence in the Deptford area. Once they were discovered research into their history has shown that black redstarts have been known to nest in the area at least intermittently since 1973, mostly on the old Deptford Power Station.

Although they were discovered on preliminary visits in the first survey year, they were not seen again until 1997 when two females (probably paired to the same male) nested, fledging a total of eight young. At the beginning of the 1998 breeding season two or possibly three males and at least two females were noted. One of the females was carrying nesting material. For a description of the birds see the *Black Redstarts of Deptford Creek* leaflet produced by the Creek Environment Project. In the early morning or late evening the males can be found singing from high perches such as cranes, chimney pots and the corners of industrial buildings. At most other times the birds are quite elusive, seen briefly perched on bollards and on Creek walls as they flycatch for food. Early in the season the males chase the females in courtship. They are quite vocal and if more than one male is present vigorous territorial skirmishes occur.

However the presence of this rare bird in the Deptford area is seriously threatened. Its liking for areas of human use makes the black redstart very vulnerable to disturbance. The present redevelopment works around the Creek mouth could cause early abandonment of nests. In the long term the loss of essential wasteland feeding habitat and the nesting opportunities provided by industrial buildings and temporary structures such as old lorries and boats present a serious threat. The homogenisation of the land which usually occurs alongside major development will not benefit the bird at all.

black redstarts and Fairview

Fairview New Homes plc., the developers of the Deptford Power Station site, accorded with the Wildlife & Countryside Act 1981 by halting works around the area where a black redstart was seen exhibiting breeding behaviour on 30th June 1997. Upon verification by a local ornithologist that the nest was off-site, work restarted on 9th July. The Act, however, does not prevent the habitat necessary to the continued survival of the bird in a local area from being destroyed.

The black redstarts rely on wasteland flora and fauna which occur sparsely along the tops of the Creek walls and in corners of the industrial plots. They cannot be considered separately from the ecology of the whole Creek. If the population is to be maintained developers need to address the particular conservation requirements of the black redstart which can act as a quality indicator for the wildlife of Creekside more generally.

mammals

A desktop survey by Mathew Frith of the **London Wildlife Trust** revealed that most of the mammals which live in Creekside would be there even if there was no Creek. However, they remain an important and visible component of the wider urban ecosystem.

urban mammals of the Creek

The highly urban character of Deptford Creek has significantly reduced its value to mammals over time, as they generally require relatively extensive areas of appropriate foraging territory in which to survive. Now only a few wild species are known from the locality, which are those species that have adapted to human imposition to a significant degree – red fox *Vulpes vulpes*, brown rat *Rattus norvegicus*, and grey squirrel *Sciurus carolinensis*, together with those who have freed themselves from domestication – feral cat *Felis domestica* and, until recently, feral dog *Canis familiaris*.

It was not always so. When the mouth of the Ravensbourne disgorged its clean waters into a wider, slower Thames among the marshy islets fringing the Creek up to 3,000 years ago, it is likely that the mammals present were those characteristic of open wetlands. These included water vole *Arvicola terrestris* and otter *Lutra lutra*. Earlier, even elk *Alces alces* and European mink *Mustela lutrola* may have been present. Small cetaceans (whales and dolphins) and pinnipeds (seals) were noted in the Thames at Deptford, for example by John Evelyn in 1652. Seals have been spotted near the Power Station Landing Stage during the recent survey period.

a 14ft whale was caught in the river Thames off Deptford in 1842

Much later, when the Creek had been bridged and a settlement established, these species would have either been hunted to extinction or lost through habitat changes, especially drainage of the marshes and wet grasslands, and eventually embankment of the Thames. In time other species made their way in to the locality – mostly livestock brought in for temporary pasture on their way to the London markets, in particular cattle, but also sheep and horses. By the 16th century, when the shipyards and docks had become an important industrial focus, other mammals found themselves new homes – the black (or ship) rat *Rattus rattus* and house mouse *Mus musculus* – living in an uneasy balance with the rat-catchers, both human and feline.

As Deptford became more urbanised from the mid-19th century, so its wild mammalian population was reduced to the most hardy – black rat, house mouse, feral cat and dog. It has only been since the collapse of the old dock and shipyard industries that constraints upon mammals have been slightly relaxed. This has been coupled with a corresponding (but unrelated) expansion of three mammals throughout most of London over the past 80 years – brown rat, red fox and grey squirrel.

bats

A bat survey by **Clive Herbert** concluded that Creekside was not a location favoured by bats. Records from the **London Bat Group** indicate only the fleeting few pipistrelles – London's most widespread bat. They can roost in buildings, but require a significant scale of open foraging habitat which can support large numbers of insects. Since the bulldozing of the Deptford Power Station site, this resource has been significantly reduced.

brown rat

The brown rat, introduced around 1728, has slowly replaced the black rat, not only along the Creek but throughout Britain, so much so that the latter is now one of the rarest wild mammals in Britain. Although the black rat may still be hanging on in a few discrete populations in London, it is extinct from Deptford. The bigger, bolder, more adaptable brown rat has taken its place. Well-acquainted with riversides and with a preference to dig shallow burrows (it is not a good climber), it is found in various industrial sites along the Creek, but not often seen due to its nocturnal behaviour. Contrary to popular opinion, the brown rat does not carry the 'plague', but is host to a water-borne virus that causes Weil's Disease, which can be dangerous. However, this is most likely in slow-moving waters, rather than the tidal Creek.

house mouse

Originally from the eastern Asian steppes, the house mouse arrived with traders from Europe, probably by the Iron Age. It rapidly adapted to an urban existence with plenty of food available, such as cereals and grains stored for baking as well as odder substances such as tallow and glue. Deptford would have been a paradise. Living a nocturnal existence, house mice were able to exploit the wide variety of nooks and crannies available to them in the early urban wood-and-wattle built environment – granaries, wharves, stables and houses. Even the use of bricks and cobbles could not stop them and, although their populations will have fluctuated due to the pressures of climate and predators such as feral cats, it has been the collapse of the old dockyard industries in Deptford and the increased concretisation that has caused their decline. Current populations are unknown but they are certainly lower than they have been for centuries. It is unlikely, however, that they will ever disappear: their great fecundity, catholic diet and small size make them a perfect mammal to exploit human habitats.

red fox

Perhaps the most readily seen of the wild mammals of the Creek, the red fox has become well and truly part of London and is found in some of the most seemingly inhospitable localities. Wastelands, railway linesides, housing estate grounds, churchyards and gardens are all host to fox earths in inner London. This is reflected in Deptford, with such sites as the Transco inlet, the railway linesides and Sue Godfrey Nature Park all being localities where foxes are often seen. Commonly assumed to be

fox cub venturing into the outside world

Bill Varney

nocturnal, foxes in urban areas are increasingly foraging during daylight hours, seemingly oblivious to their human observers. The fox population is currently affected with mange, which in Bristol became pandemic and reduced the population by over 95% in a few years. Whilst many local foxes exhibit mange, there is little indication as yet that it is significantly affecting numbers.

human users

Deptford Creek is a rare quiet urban space well loved by a number of human users. These range from families living on boats, through father-and-son anglers, to teenagers looking for privacy and enthusiasts looking for wildlife. As a navigable waterway it attracts boating use from established boat-based residents and visiting craft. Creekside is home to one of the few industries which still use the river for transport. Portia Smith of the **Deptford Discovery Team** undertook a series of taped interviews with the people who live and work on the Creek.

the family boaters

Mike Canty & Maureen Chapple

Mike lives on his 75ft Humber Keel boat with Maureen and their two teenage sons, Ciaran and Liam. He has a workshop in a lighter craft moored alongside. Mike bought his first barge in 1966 and fitted it out himself as a home. He says life has never been the same since.

Mike rents a workspace from Skillion's Business Centre. He gets mail there and water and electricity from the offices. His situation is typical of river-living in London, tucked behind industrial sites. The deal with Skillion's is not secure and the family have no rights at all. Mike and Maureen pay their council tax in Greenwich but they have to pay for rubbish collection twice as it is included as part of the rent. Skillion's could not make them move but they could turn off the water and power, which would destroy his livelihood as well as his home.

Barking Canoe Club bring canoes up once a month on the rising tide. Once a year around 15 narrow-boats visit the Creek. They come out at Limehouse, head upriver to Grand Union Canal and pop up the Creek on the tide to say hello. It is quite difficult to turn in the Creek and they don't have long. Mike said it would be possible for them to set down but they don't know it is safe. Sometimes passing yachts come up the Creek to explore but the shore is totally inaccessible to visitors.

Caroline Lister

Ciaran Canty learning the ropes

Access to the Creek is very limited. Mike hopes that the new education and visitor centre and proposed overnight services for boaters by the Hoy Stairs will improve this. It would be easy to use canoes and small sailing dinghies in the Creek but the river bed needs to be cleared of dangerous debris. It will never attract a lot of people, but offers a great half-hour trip. Too often development diminishes the mooring options and huge 'NO MOORINGS' signs appear. Yet Deptford Creek has the potential to be improved for boaters. Dowell's Wharf could house a historic boat that actually sails. Theatre Arm could be for residential boats, with dinghies and canoeing in the basin.

In the evening teenagers climb onto the train tracks at Greenwich station and walk along to the railway bridge where they climb down onto the central pier to fish. Teenagers also hang out around the back of Booker's Cash and Carry where they sit and watch the water.

"There is an attraction to the water – peaceful, quiet, romantic, calming. You develop a lifestyle of protecting it."

Maureen finds it difficult to compare life on board with a landlubber's existence. "When the kids were tiny not having a garden was a problem and we couldn't just say 'go on deck' because they might fall in. When the tide was out there was a shingle beach and they made mud pies. Everyone worried they'd get some dreadful disease but they're the healthiest children I know. They had a great time, although they always looked like little ruffians".

For Maureen living on a boat has its own rewards, including meals on deck. "We watch the tide going in and out, watch the ducks and swans, we're very aware of what is going on out there." But there are problems. "If you leave the skylight open when you go to work, you come back to a soaking wet bed. If you go away you have to have someone come and stay on board. We came back once after a day out to find this party picnicking on deck: mum, dad and two kids. They just thought it was some old boat." Ciaran is not certain that he would like to live on a boat when he's older, but if he does it will be "done up properly".

Julian Kingston & Jeannie Seymour

Julian lives on Motor Vessel *Sabine,* a 1922 German sea defences inspection vessel of 74ft, with his wife, Jeannie, and his son, Joshua. *Sabine* is unique. She looks a bit like a trawler and was used as a fishing boat after the war. Julian's grand plan is to finish the wheel house and deck and then take *Sabine* to the Friesland Islands where she was built.

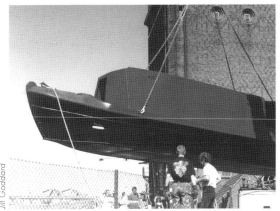

Julian recently his son a narrow-boat at the Creekside site in order to give him a home of his own

The family used to moor behind the Bird's Nest pub, alongside his brother's film catering company. DLR arranged for them to moor at the Lewisham College site until the railway is finished when they can go back to Theatre Arm Wharf. He hopes to buy the wharf from his brother but will not be able to put a workshop on it because of the railway viaduct.

Julian finds applying for bank cards or credit cards is difficult as soon as you mention the word 'boat'. He feels this is ridiculous as the radar system covering the channel and the North Sea makes it much easier to find a boat. They can seize your boat much more easily than sending the bailiff to a house.

The latest annual report from the SRB says Creekside will become part of London's Gateway. Julian thinks until there are facilities for passing boats this won't happen. Boaters need more than just water, power supplies and moorings; they need chandleries, rope and sail makers, stainless steel fitting makers, pontoon makers, and so on. To attract such businesses the local authorities could offer concessions such as cheap rates.

The two projects that should be pushed most strongly are the Ha'penny Hatch and the Education Centre. Both are "brilliant projects – the bridge will get walkers down and the centre will get everyone involved and provide access". He thinks the key aim should be to get people with boats to start using the Creek rather than getting local people to use boats. That will create interest and the crossover will start.

Jeannie and Julian met three years ago and from the moment she set foot on the boat she felt like she was stepping into a fairy tale. She had never imagined living anywhere without a garden but the Creek is her garden now, with more diverse wildlife than any garden.

The way the tide moves objects around is always interesting. The seasons have their way of changing the Creek too. The algae in the summer months make beautiful colours. Jeannie loves the stillness when the tide is in, even though there is heavy traffic close by. However to have the tide in all the time would seem sterile, like living in a marina which they had to do last year. She loves the luxury of both boating on the Creek and walking it at low tides.

Rainer Cole
Rainer lives on a 100 ft fishing trawler at Dowell's Wharf. He also owns an enormous minesweeper which he would like to turn into a performance/art space. He pays for access across land and to park a car on the scrapyard. There is no legal tenancy or agreement. Local developer, Len Wallis, owns the site and Rainer was not sure if there would be a problem when the building work starts.

Rainer says there is a good community feel to the people who use the Creek; for example the crane driver from Prior's helped him to lift a boat with the crane. The Prior's boat crews always give a friendly wave as they come past. There are kids who fish from the boat named the *Black Death*. One man and his son used to come down every day to fish. "Sometimes when the tide is coming in the water looks alive with fish. I see heron, ducks and seagulls feeding at low tide. I really enjoy taking people out in the boat, showing them the Creek."

Kids breaking in can be a problem so they put a lock on the gate. Usually they don't come in to steal; they are looking for footballs amongst the flotsam or they want to have a go on a dinghy. "It's great that they have an interest in the river and would be brilliant if there was somewhere they could do it safely. One resident of Hughesfield estate takes her child down to the beach but many of the children on the estate are told not to go down there because it is dangerous. Some Sundays there are lots of people walking on Deptford beach."

"There has to be something wrong with you to live on a boat" according to Rainer. Like Mike, Rainer did all the building and repairs on the boat. Most of the materials came from skips. All the Creek boaters tend to hoard things and their boats are littered with bits of interesting junk. Rainer said that all his clothes smell of diesel, another consequence of boat living.

Alf Harman
Alf has lived on the Creek since 1989. He also has a flat. When he first arrived he was working for a set design company in the Skillion's Business Centre and lived in an old lifeboat at the back of Skillion's.

Alf recently salvaged a 76 ft motor fishing vessel called *Northern Star* from Dreadnought Wharf. The PLA gave the owner notice and when the time of notice elapsed they sold her to Alf. Raising her took three months and involved pumping water into the hull at every tide, stirring it up to move the mud and then pumping out the slurry with a mud pump.

Alf wants to complete the work on *Northern Star* and make her sea-going. He would like to use the Creek as his home mooring but has no security of tenure. The future looks uncertain. When he first arrived he was alone on the Creek, living under the canvas of his lifeboat for four years at the back of Skillion's, who saw him as a useful security asset for the site. Any new access to boat moorings would have to be locked to stop kids climbing on the boats.

The Watergate project within the Creekside Renewal SRB is proposing new residential moorings on the Thames frontage, west of the Creek mouth. Alf is worried that expensive boats will increase the theft on moorings which is not much of a problem at present. Boatyards are dangerous places for children if they are unsupervised. Alf likes it the way it is at the moment, not too many boats. Alf has offered his lifeboat to use as a skip for collecting the rubbish in the Creek as it is cleared.

the industrial users

J J Prior's Associates

John Greenleaf is the operations manager of Prior's, based on the Greenwich bank close to Creek Bridge. Each of Prior's boats can carry 300 tonnes of aggregate. Lorries on London Red Routes are restricted to just over 20 tonnes, so each boat is equivalent to 15 lorries. Prior's have five boats and have recently averaged 3,500 tonnes a week. He is surprised by the number of people who stand on Creek Bridge watching Prior's boats negotiating in and out.

The other end of Prior's operations is in Colchester where they have their own gravel pit. They dig the gravel, load it into their own boats and ship it to concrete-makers. The beauty of the operation is that Ready Mix Concrete are Prior's tenants on the Creekside site and also an important customer. To make concrete you need aggregate, sand, cement, water and a big mixer. Prior's supply the gravel and sand for the concrete which RMC mix on site. RMC are going to buy a cement tanker so all the components of the concrete will come by river without lorry movements and the concrete is available close to the major Greenwich developments. Concrete all has to be poured at the same time. A lorry can only hold six metres of concrete yet some of the DLR works involved 200-300 meter pours.

The Creek is a very useful waterway commercially and an asset to both boroughs. Greenwich Council are now sympathetic to Prior's because of the lorry ban and an understanding of how much traffic they are keeping off the roads. John feels the Creek should be used more. Prior's have always used boats and are governed by the tides. Last year they received a Freight Facilities Grant to assist with purchase and refitting of the new *Peter Prior* for sand and aggregate transportation. This will take 12,000 lorry journeys off roads in the South East in the next two years. John would like to see all the money saved on not building motorways ploughed into other forms of transport. He has seen a change in the last ten years; not much action but attitudes are definitely changing. The Millennium celebrations will make transport on the river a real issue for access to and from the Dome site.

Penny Metal

Jeff Paul working his crane

Jeff Paul drives Prior's crane, which is possibly the oldest working crane still operating on the Thames, built by Stothert and Pit in the early 1960s. He has worked there for 30 years, starting off as a labourer before becoming the crane driver like his father.

Greenwich Council organise the lifting of Creek Bridge. An Act of Parliament when the bridge was built means they have to give access two hours before and one hour after high tide. Prior's boats usually creep in under the bridge but when they leave they have to raise the bridge as they are unloaded and therefore higher in the water. It takes about two hours to unload a boat. School parties and other groups often stand on the bridge watching Jeff unloading and wave.

In the past Prior's have had meetings with residents due to complaints about noise. They have since fitted rubbers to the grab but the tides mean they have to unload at odd times, sometimes one or two o'clock in the morning. "We don't go out to make a lot of noise, but the scraping from the bottom can be noisy. These people who buy the lovely houses by the riverside move in. A fortnight later they start complaining about the noise, a few barges banging along the banks. It's like living next to a farm and complaining about the smell. That is a farm, isn't it?"

There is a plan to move Prior's further up the Creek to Gordino's yard which is around 30% bigger than the current yard but Jeff is in two minds as to whether this is a good idea. If they did move, the crane would stay. It is a standard dockside crane, but they are few and far between nowadays. It would cost too much to relocate and convert it to a moving crane on tracks. Prior's is a protected working wharf and any change of use would have to be agreed by the Department for the Environment, Transport & the Regions (DETR). The proposal would involve transferring the protected wharf status to the new site. Jeff feels that people accept Prior's in its current spot. "If we move up there and all of a sudden at 3am there's all this noise people who live there will complain because it's new."

Jeff loves the wildlife of the Creek. When the tide goes out the propellers make a big hole where fish get trapped. Sometimes he sees fox cubs playing in the sand bin. "Any dirty industry should have a few trees round it. But there's lots of plants along the river wall. It will be nice when the hotel and liner terminal is built. In ten years time you won't recognise the place. We'll still be here though, we've got a building boom. People say they don't want dirty industries here but they want the houses."

Gordino's

Gordino's is a waste management company for local authorities. They have been based on the Greenwich bank of the Creek midway between Creek Road and the railway bridge for five years. The company is owned by Brian Huckle and his partner Brian Glascock.

Brian Huckle says he only notices the Creek in the winter when the wind blows along it. He thinks the Creek should be dredged, the walls repaired, the rubbish removed and a barrage installed to keep the water in. They could let the rubbish out in a rush at low tide then shut the gates again. "The mud is a joke when the tide is out. A barrage would bring more boats. Lots of boats can't get up there anymore. The railway bridge used to lift to let boats through but now it is fixed they can't go up the Creek anymore. At present the Creek doesn't really serve any purpose. They could make it into a marina. You have to find a happy medium with development. Do you want it for wildlife or boats?"

Brian said they lost a dog over the side of the Creek a few years ago, "a lovely dog, good temperament, only two years old. He must have seen a fox, went chasing after it, jumped in the Creek. We found the body next day on the other side of the Creek."

Until recently Gordino's had not explored the possibility of using barges for transportation in any detail but increased traffic delays and potential gridlock, pressure from the environmental lobby and grants to equalise costs between road and river transport are forcing them to rethink. A major customer is located on the north shore of the Thames and has a marine division geared to handling water transport. Traffic forecasts for the year 2000 have indicated at least 40% more traffic using the A102(M) so potential disruption associated with the Millennium celebrations may make river transport an attractive option.

Repairs to the river walls are a major concern to riverside owners. For a site like Gordino's where there is no change of use the Environment Agency will contribute up to 90% if they approve the designs. While Gordino's favour the most cost-effective solution, the EA will only fund high quality work which has a long life and is environmentally acceptable. Plain steel sheet piling is no longer acceptable and would not receive the necessary Land Drainage Consent. There is a clause in the contract which means if Gordino's develop the site or sell it within ten years they will have to pay back a decreasing proportion of the costs of the river walls.

renewal

renewal without destruction

The thin green line is in danger of being erased. Having been ignored for half a century, and gloriously allowed to decay, Deptford Creek is now a shining glint in the eye of the developer. The ragged edges of the Creek which mother nature took back for her own do not fit well with stark modern designs of waterside apartments, galleries, bistros and hotels, drawings of which now litter the planners' offices. The precarious growth from rotten piles and overhanging vegetation appears tatty and untidy to the engineer or builder tasked with regenerating this forgotten backwater.

Unfortunately the historical and ecological significance of Deptford Creek's meandering dereliction and decline is easily lost on a property developer. Encouraged by both local and national government to inject new money and new vitality into what is seen by many as a disadvantaged urban system, the developer wants a clean and prestigious structure to offer to his clients. With Deptford so close to the Greenwich Meridian and Millennium site, pressure is on to establish plans quickly in a fertile investment environment. As one of the last remaining undeveloped waterfronts in London, Deptford is seen as a ripe financial fruit, ready for plucking.

For the developer, Deptford Creek has one overriding characteristic which complicates any plans to build – its tidal nature. The very quality which makes it an attractive site – picturesque views over the water – also makes it an expensive option. For in London, where there is tidal flow and the threat of tidal flooding, there has to be flood defence. As the Creek walls are crumbling, any developer first has to invest heavily in repairing and rebuilding them. It has been the developers' desire for the cheapest and easiest option (steel sheet piling), which has often polarised the debate on how the Creek should be renewed and regenerated.

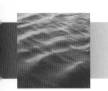

Modern building practice is all about bulldozers and other heavy machinery. A look at the last two decades of building work on the Thames frontage and in London's Docklands shows little if any sympathy with the 'environment' which is constrained in a few turfed lawn areas and some tiny stylised garden plots of very limited ecological interest. The small but complex communities of plants and animals which have developed in the fringing habitats of Deptford Creek are a rare diversion from the mundane banks of the River Thames. But their value is masked by their insignificance appearance. What investor wants to bother with a few bits of bedraggled herbage, a few tweety-birds and some rather dull-looking bugs? Such is the ethos permeating much of the building industry. Perhaps the driving aim of the Creek Environment Project has been to influence this opinion and to encourage a more sympathetic approach to developing the much underrated habitat of urban 'wasteland' or 'brownfield' sites.

But times are changing. Sympathy for the environment is increasingly seen as an important consideration by a general public who daily read about the destruction of the rainforest and the disappearance of the ozone layer. Deptford Creek is a far cry from these global issues, but its value as an ecologically important site has nevertheless been recognised, and the need to take account of the 'legacy' and 'life' of local areas is now widely argued.

This argument has mainly centred around mitigation, the building industry's jargon for environmental damage limitation. The notion behind this is that whenever an area is developed it should include specific designs in the structures of buildings and the flood defence walls, to encourage the wildlife that was there before and to offset any habitat destruction by creating new opportunities for animals and plants to recolonise. It all starts being fairly straightforward: the ecologists see continuity and a certain amount of habitat replacement; the local authority planners see 'best practice' achieved and sympathetic, less damaging, development; the builders get publicity and kudos from the habitat-enhancing features of their worthy designs and sensitive landscaping.

However, all this is a very new approach. Designers are unsure how to incorporate the ecologists' ideas of bird-nesting nooks and silt-filled crannies into their river walls. It is so much easier to get a junior draughtsman to come up with a standard bleak design 'by the book'. Builders worry that it might cost more to implement enhancements, and the developers feel that it imposes even more complicated planning restrictions on what they would like to create.

Conflict is already in the air. Redevelopment is already in progress, planning permissions have been given for some sites and some building work started. With the discovery of black redstarts in the Creek area, attempts were made to influence designs already passed and approved, to enlarge the area of foraging habitat available, to modify planting schemes, to increase nest site opportunities and generally to encourage these nationally scarce and protected birds. Such changes so far down the line are annoying and difficult for the developers. Mistrust creeps in as to the reality of these 'sightings'. What area does such a small bird really need to survive? It is far better if negotiations can include such opportunities at an early design stage.

Fortunately, the Environment Agency, which controls and approves the flood defence walls, already has its own agenda of enhancement ideas. The EA actively promotes ecological continuity and habitat improvement in its own works, and also regulates third party works. River wall repair at the Millennium site further down the Thames has already established principles of habitat creation and improvement. Work has yet to begin on any Creek walls, but at least the spirit of environmental enhancement is in place.

the Lower Creek showing many aspects of the Creekside landscape during the period of transition

barrage

One key study was carried out in the early stages of the bid preparation and, indeed, was the reason for the involvement of Lewisham Nature Conservation Team. Jill Goddard was asked to advise on the cost of an environmental impact assessment as part of a study into putting a barrage across the Creek mouth. "That was when I realised how dangerous it was that people was talking about changing the Creek with no real understanding of what it was about."

Following the preparation of the Creekside Strategy, **W S Atkins** were commissioned in July 1994 by Lewisham and Greenwich Councils to investigate the economic, social and environmental impacts of various barrier and 'no barrier' options for environmental enhancements of Deptford Creek.

techniques

A 1988 engineering study by Rendel Palmer and Tritton for a barrier at the mouth of the Creek had considered two options:

- an uncontrolled weir involving a low concrete sill which would maintain a minimum water level at all times but with regular tidal intrusion
- a sill with a control gate which would maintain a high and relatively constant water level but could be lowered to allow the passage of floods. With this design the tide is excluded by raising the gates and the pond would be of freshwater.

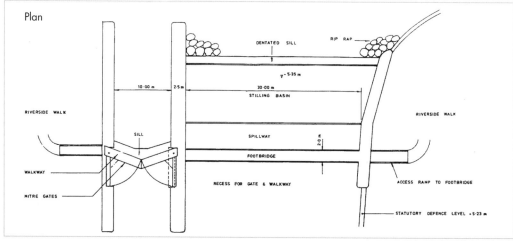

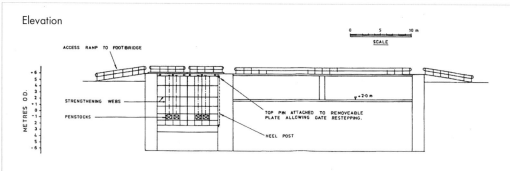

designs by Rendel Palmer & Tritton for the uncontrolled weir. These were used by W S Atkins to evaluate the costs and benefits of impounding the Creek.

Both options included a lock to accommodate vessels up to 29.5 m in length with a 2 m draught. These were the designs used by W S Atkins in their study.

Four locations were identified for evaluation of barrier options
- at the Creek mouth
- adjacent to Creek Road bridge
- adjacent to the railway bridge
- at Evelyn Wharf

At Evelyn Wharf only an uncontrolled weir was proposed; at each of the others both an uncontrolled and a gated structure were considered. In addition, at the Creek mouth an option was identified involving a gated structure with penstocks to attenuate tidal fluctuations.

For comparative evaluation the study defined a 'no barrier' option of environmental enhancements. This entailed the removal of debris and the creation of intertidal habitats with side terraces at various locations to encourage marshland plants tolerant of brackish conditions, principally common reed *Phragmites australis*, the grey bulrush *Schoenoplectus tabernaemontani* and sea club rush *Scirpus maritimus*. The waterside community could be supplemented by terrestrial plantings, perhaps in a raised bed along the edge of the wharves. Alongside the wild hop already present, W S Atkins suggested similar wild creepers such as honeysuckle, bryony and traveller's joy along, with trees and shrubs such as crack willow, hawthorn, blackthorn, buckthorn, wild rose, privet and broom. It was suggested that some new plantings should be connected to existing vegetation, for example along the railway line, to create larger habitat units which could connect to areas beyond the Creek.

The study also involved a review of the actual socio-economic and environmental effects of two existing barriers (Rivers Wandle and Tawe) and the predicted effects of three proposed barriers (Rivers Roding, Usk and Tees). Consultation with 27 statutory and local agencies was an integral part of the study, and the appendix of notes from meetings and telephone conversations makes for an interesting historic document.

The evaluation of the socio-economic costs and benefits of the barrier included:
- consideration of the regeneration objectives for the area
- estimation of the development potential of Creekside
- the production of development scenarios for the area under each of the options
- quantification of costs and benefits (output measures) generated by each scenario
- evaluation of each option against a series of economic performance indicators.

The following potential benefits were considered:
- development effects
- land/property brought into development which would otherwise not have been
- accelerated/enhanced level of lettings/sales of vacant property to end users
- enhanced land/property values
- other economic benefits
- net gains in direct employment from development
- increased employment from visitor expenditure
- increased diversification of uses
- improved image profile for existing businesses
- improved confidence in the area.

The basic assumption that the more of the river is impounded the greater the employment and development impact, was dependent on conditions such as availability and location of development land, the sensitivity of the proposed land use to the presence or absence of a barrier, and the impact of the option on existing businesses.

findings

The review of barrier projects revealed that substantial socio-economic benefits were often predicted but rarely borne out. Visual enhancement was claimed in all cases to offset concerns about the hydrology and ecology of impounded rivers, though W S Atkins recognised differences of opinion as to whether impoundment represents an enhancement.

With few schemes implemented and even fewer studies of their effects, there was little hard evidence for the benefits claimed, though occasionally a case could be made for a barrier as part of a package of initiatives to promote economic regeneration. In the case of the Wandle barrier, no impact studies were undertaken, although the promoters saw it as a catalyst to riverside commercial and residential development. In 1994, two and a half years after construction, no development had taken place, there was no evidence of any socio-economic benefits, and proposals for water-based leisure had yet to be implemented.

Consultation showed limited support for a barrier at Deptford Creek, primarily from landowners and developers, from the PLA Head of Leisure & Tourism and from some council officers. They saw impoundment as one element in upgrading the image of Creekside and boosting investor confidence, although a barrier in itself would not be a sufficient catalyst to stimulate regeneration. Serious reservations were expressed by the PLA (loss of navigation rights and the protection of Prior's) and by the NRA and English Nature (environmental grounds).

W S Atkins' description of the likely environmental effects of barriers derived mainly from predictive modelling. The specialised and characteristic fauna and flora of estuaries are adapted to the daily changes in water levels, salinity and exposure. Barriers convert this periodic system to a stable and predominantly freshwater system. The marine and brackish flora and fauna give way to freshwater communities as found in lakes and ponds. Birds lose feeding areas on the former mudflats, marine fish lose their spawning and nursery areas and the movement of migratory fish is impeded. Without tidal flushing, nutrients and pollutants can accumulate behind the barrier. The water temperature increases, reducing oxygen levels, increasing fish mortality and encouraging algal bloom. Sedimentation builds up as the volume and speed of flow decrease and these changes may affect fish as well as release any pollutants locked into the sediment. Impounded water also produces a rise in the local water table which may effect the terrestrial ecology, the built environment, the integrity of underground services and the conservation of archaeological sites.

Environment Agency

the Wandle half-tide weir had severe environmental impacts and none of the predicted regeneration benefits

At the Wandle barrier W S Atkins found that siltation had increased by 1.8 m, deterring wading birds, attracting insects and causing an odour, while increased scouring in the Thames had destabilised river walls. It was understood that the London Borough of Wandsworth was considering removing the barrier because of its failure to meet objectives and the high maintenance costs incurred.

"The Wandle half tide weir was constructed in 1990 to maintain a level of water in the mouth of the Wandle and cover 'unsightly mudflats'. It was thought that this would improve the amenity of the area and encourage early development. Problems with the original construction meant the weir had to be rebuilt. Until recently, it has been in the 'off position' most of the time because it was impairing the performance of a demonstration micro-turbine further upstream. Nevertheless it has caused considerable siltation. The bed of the Wandle, which was mainly gravel, has now been covered by a layer of silt. The Environment Agency wish to see the weir removed, because of siltation and general ecological degradation, and have offered to make a contribution. Their ecological arguments appear convincing. The principal local amenity group, the Wandsworth Society, wish to keep the weir because some leading members want boating activities at all times in the lower Wandle and Bell Lane Creek.
The matter remains unresolved. A study, as yet unpublished, was carried out by the Technical Services department to establish the necessary regime for de-silting the river. This suggests expensive work every five years. The consultancy currently working with the Wandsworth Challenge Partnership to produce a Riverbank Improvement Plan for the Wandle delta area have suggested an immediate assessment of environmental and regeneration effects." (Wandsworth Council update, January 1999)

At Deptford Creek the minimum cost option to secure environmental enhancement was the 'no barrier' option which had the lowest cost per job and the highest public sector leverage ratio. This option also had the least potential environmental impact while, of the barrier options, those closest to the Creek mouth were predicted to have most impact. It is interesting that W S Atkins acknowledged in this early report that "relatively little appears to be known of the ecological characteristics of the Creek" (they listed 18 plant species). They suggested further studies of invertebrates, fish populations, bird life and sediment pollutants.

The major proposed developments at Greenwich Reach East and the Power Station site did not depend at all on the construction of a barrier, nor did the extension of the DLR. Thus any socio-economic benefits induced by a barrier would be marginal in comparison. The study concluded that any enhanced development attributable to a barrier would be minimal. The benefits were evaluated using two performance ratios: public sector capital cost per job and public sector to private sector leverage. The 'no barrier' option gave a cost of £20,000 for each job and leverage at 1:2.25. Any additional benefits to be derived from a barrier at the Creek mouth would cost £95,000 per job and generate additional leverage of only 1:0.56.

In considering social costs and impacts, the study stressed that the amenity value of the Creekside area for the local community and visitors would only increase with greater access. The scope for water-based recreation was uncertain given that water quality in an impounded Creek may not be safe. Open water also carried the possibility of accidents, although improved safety facilities and increased usage would offset this.

Overall the 'no barrier' option ranked highest in cost-effective regeneration, job creation, investment leverage and environmental enhancement, with minimum adverse impacts. A few voices, including the Inland Waterways Association and the road-based waste disposal firm Gordino's, continue to argue for impoundment, but the Creekside Renewal SRB programme was founded on the premise that Deptford Creek would remain a tidal river.

*f*lood defence

Deptford Creek, as the tidal part of the River Ravensbourne, is affected by the tidal level in the River Thames at all times and experiences high and low tides twice a day. Several times a month high tides (called 'spring' tides) exceed the level of the adjacent land in many places up the Creek, and if it were not for the flood defences these areas would be regularly inundated.

Sometimes spring tides can be higher than they would normally be, when weather conditions create a surge in the North Sea, and this surge is funnelled into the Thames Estuary. In extreme cases the Thames Barrier would then be closed, but there are several other times each year when Creek high tide levels are higher than the normal monthly spring tides. The need for raised defences at all points along the Creek becomes apparent for anyone who can see high water.

Although sea level rise is now a fact, the need for raised defences has been recognised for many years, as has the vulnerability of Thames-side communities to flooding if the river walls were not maintained and kept to an appropriate height. In 1879 an Act of Parliament was passed which required riparian owners of the tidal Thames and tributaries to raise their defences to defined levels, and to maintain them, for the safety of the wider community.

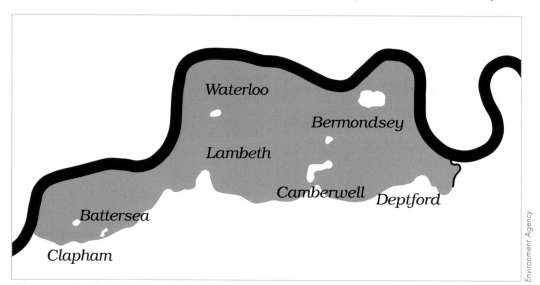

Environment Agency

if the west wall of the Creek was breached, London would flood as far as Clapham

The Environment Agency (EA) is the Government body given permissive powers to carry out flood defence works to protect the general public from flood damage and to enforce legislation aimed at safeguarding existing defences. In the tidal Thames it has become obvious that, with the decline of the river as a commercial port, many riparian owners simply cannot afford to maintain their frontages to the standard required by the 1879 Act. In recognition that the flood defences on these frontages protect far more than the riparian owner's individual property, the EA can use public money to repair and renew the defences that are in imminent danger of failure.

The forerunners of the EA included the Greater London Council, Thames Water and the National Rivers Authority. Whilst the original focus of flood defence was on hard engineering works, with little consideration for aesthetics or the environment, over the transition period to the EA the emphasis shifted to working with nature far more than in the past. Indeed, one of the EA's duties is to enhance the environment in all its activities.

In Deptford Creek the years of intense commercial usage, both within the Creek and on the banks, have resulted in vertical walls practically everywhere. These walls are primarily retaining walls – holding up the property next to the Creek, and preventing it from falling into the Creek bed. However, in order to maximise their useful land, riparian owners have invariably raised these retaining walls to the required flood defence level, rather than having lower retaining walls and constructing a flood defence wall or bank away from the river. (This situation would, of course, allow some of the land to flood occasionally).

The Environment Agency can carry out capital works to any defences that are deemed to have a remaining useful life of less than five years, and carries out regular inspections to identify such defences. In 1996 the EA commissioned the **Babtie Group** to carry out the necessary survey and inspections of the Deptford Creek frontages and to report on the options for those frontages where work was felt to be necessary.

techniques

In order to identify accurately the defences at risk of failure, Babtie carried out detailed inspections to all 54 Creek frontages, totalling 2400m, both from the landward side and from a boat in the Creek. Each frontage has a unique number (see the map on page vii). A team of engineers and a geotechnical specialist was involved in the work, which included the investigation of all cracks, holes, evidence of movement, and general condition of materials. For specialist investigation of the timber piles that form many walls, a timber expert from the Building Research Establishment was subsequently called in.

Level surveys were carried out by Babtie, not only to confirm the level of the existing flood defence but also to determine the levels of land behind the frontage. This can give an indication of the depth and frequency of potential inundation should a defence fail.

Each frontage – or sub-frontage where construction varied along a frontage – was catalogued in terms of land ownership, construction materials, any specific features (outfalls, flap valves, etc.), structural condition, and, most importantly, an estimate of the remaining useful life of the flood defence.

The inspections did not, however, look solely at the engineering aspects of the flood defence. An environmental team was also involved in assessing, from Creek and from land, the important ecological, landscape and heritage features of the frontages.

findings

A preliminary report by Babtie, dated April 1997, includes a table which summarises the information gained by the site surveys. Types of frontage were mainly steel sheet piling, timber walls (often repaired with concrete, giving the appearance of a concrete wall), brick and concrete. Not surprisingly, the older and more derelict walls, generally timber, were those which provided habitats for the widest range of flora and invertebrates.

Three sections of Deptford Creek can be defined:
- downstream section (Lower Creek) close to the Thames
- middle section between Creek Road and the railway bridge
- upstream section (Upper Creek) from the railway bridge to the sills at Deptford Bridge.

downstream section

This part, downstream of Creek Road, is where the Creek opens out to the Thames. The area is dominated by large industrial plots, most of which were cleared or derelict at the time of the survey. The frontages are mainly raked timber and concrete, although there is some sheet steel piling.

middle section

The industrial plots in this section are generally smaller than those downstream, sandwiched between the Creek and the roads (Creekside, Copperas Street and Norman Road) which run parallel to it. Frontages are similar to those downstream, although with a greater proportion of old timber walls.

upstream section

Upstream of the railway bridge plot sizes are smaller, with a higher density of buildings. Although similar frontages to those downstream occur in this section, there are also a number of old brick wharves. The frontage of Thames Water's pumping station site is described as being "of elegant detailed cast-iron panels with coursed stone on top, sadly this impressive part of this distinguished Victorian development has been spoilt by the addition of concrete coping and galvanised palisade fencing". This section of the Creek also includes more 'boating furniture' than downstream – mooring rings, chains, and ladders can be found, although not all in a functional state.

Once the survey work was complete Babtie were able to categorise all frontages where remedial or repair work was likely to be needed as high priority (work required as soon as possible), medium priority (work required within 15 years), or low priority (work not required for at least 15 years). The category into which any given frontage fell was subjective, but based on the professional judgements of experienced civil and geotechnical engineers.

Eight high priority frontages were identified with an estimated life of less than five years and thus urgently needing repair or renewal. These were:

DC07 Thanet Wharf (Salter's). The existing wall is a dilapidated timber construction, with vegetation growing out of the wall where timber boards have disintegrated.

DC12 Normandy Wharf (Sentinel's). This is similar to Thanet Wharf, above, except that there are substantial old crane rail foundations on piles immediately behind the decaying frontage.

DC15 Transco Inlet (British Gas Transco). This small frontage has a brick wall, nearly collapsed in places and heavily overgrown with vegetation. The foreshore in front of the wall is gradually being eroded.

DC43 Saxon Wharf (Gordino's). Similar to Thanet Wharf, although at the upstream end the frontage has been built across an old draw-dock, which was then infilled.

DC44 Hilton's Wharf (Claygreen Ltd). This comprises a timber wall with horizontal boards between king piles. A repair was attempted with sprayed concrete (gunite) in the past, but this is itself now failing, exposing the rotten timber and large gaps where backfill can be eroded.

S396 Creek Mouth West (Fairview New Homes). The original wall was of timber construction, although part has been replaced by steel sheet piles. Much of the timber wall is now in a poor state of repair, particularly near the high water mark, where timber planks are missing, allowing the backfill to wash out.

S397 Greenwich Reach East (Clearwater Development). Again, a composite wall showing signs of previous repairs.

S398 Dreadnought Wharf (Clearwater Development). This is a Thames frontage, and thus subject to greater boat- and wind-generated wave attack than frontages within the Creek. Erosion of the old timber frontage has taken place to the extent that the wall was being undermined.

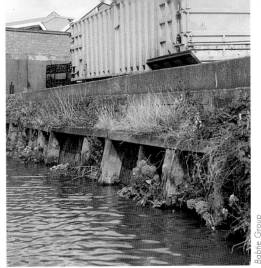

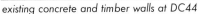

existing concrete and timber walls at DC44   existing timber ledge at DC44

These frontages generally coincided with those providing the greatest ecological and habitat value, as it is only when the walls are in a deteriorated state that habitats are created. Good environmental design is now aiming to mimic these habitats on new walls.

A further 32 frontages were identified where some remedial works would be needed, but these were not the highest priority. In most cases the work would involve replacing timber fenders and making good cracks and holes.

further monitoring

Although action is now planned for the eight priority frontages, the other frontages within Deptford Creek cannot be ignored. All tidal Thames frontages will have to be inspected every five years and a new set of priority works drawn up.

A new round of investigations, proposals and consultations will then take place, building on the knowledge gained from the current works. This will be especially true for the built-in environmental enhancements. Do they work as intended? Could an alternative be tried? What lessons can be learned?

impacts of development

Most developers see the Creek waterfront as a nuisance rather than an opportunity. Many would like to encroach further into the Creek than has been done over past decades and centuries. Others shift the focus of development inwards, turning their backs on the Creek.

The EA has limited powers, mainly relating to works in, on or over the Creek, and activities within 16 metres of the top of the bank. In addition, the EA is a statutory consultee to the planning authorities, but the latter have no specific duty to heed any such comments.

The EA much prefers to work closely with developers before a planning application is submitted so that a solution encompassing the development as a whole can be worked up. Such a solution should take into consideration the Creek setting and the opportunities which that provides; potential enhancements to ecology and landscape; and the legal requirements of flood defence. Environment Agency staff are very willing to input into the pre-application process, and have a great deal of experience and ideas to offer in support of a sustainable, environmentally-sensitive development proposal.

themes

Robert West Consulting were commissioned to collect and collate the existing information relating to the ecology, river processes, heritage, river walls and usage of Deptford Creek and develop options for the enhancement of the Creek environment.

techniques

This was a very broad survey encompassing many different elements. It outlined the current character and usage of the three main Creek sections, noting known development plans and referring to buildings of note in the immediate environs. Features which should be preserved, enhanced and developed in the local landscape were identified. A habitat map was created through those baseline ecological surveys available at the time and by surveying areas of the Creek at high and low tides. Available data on flow, water quality and channel siltation was analysed and areas of erosion and siltation in the channel bed identified. Existing fixtures and fittings (mooring rings, safety chains, ladders and drainage outlets) were mapped to identify possible berths and the business potential, demand and physical feasibility of new marine facilities were assessed. Rubbish, outfalls and potential sources of pollution or polluting activity were identified via surveys and through public registers held by local authorities, the Environment Agency and the Health & Safety Executive. Current uses of the Creek channel and plans for changes of use emerged through questionnaire consultation in partnership with the Land Use study.

The survey then developed a series of options for environmental enhancements along with cost estimates, visualisations and liability assessments for the favoured options for enhancement, access and river use facilities.

findings

The report identified three broad approaches to the future use of the Creek.

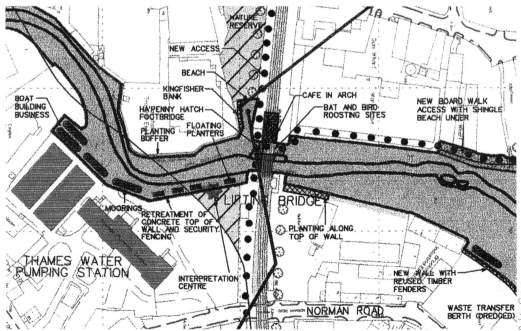

central Creek detail from the 'possible combined use' consultation map

industrial heritage and ecology

The Creek as a nature reserve and industrial heritage area. Access is limited and use of the Creek waterway minimised to avoid disturbing the fauna. River walls are maintained using traditional materials and techniques, with re-use and restoration of bollards, mooring rings and other marine equipment wherever possible. This approach benefits the wildlife and those studying the ecology of the Creek and preserves its post-industrial character. Existing Creek users would not be disturbed but no new usage would be encouraged.

Proposals would include enhancing habitats for invertebrates, marine borers, birds, fish and other fauna by re-use of existing timber and the creation of new banks, islands and areas of tranquillity. The Creek would be cleaned as far as possible without disturbing pollution and existing valued habitats. There would be new planting to the Creek walls and floating planters. Opportunities would be sought to create sloped banks to take advantage of the rich habitats these can create.

access and recreation

The Creek as a recreation resource with access points, riverside walks and facilities for boating, fishing and canoeing. Development of attractions which bring maximum visitors. This approach could benefit the whole community and particularly those groups which use the education centre. The existing flora and fauna would be disturbed.

Proposals would include a cafe at the railway arch with an education and recreation centre to allow boat storage, access to the watercourse, walkways and bridges throughout the area, and opportunities for visitors to learn about the Creek. A boat service pontoon and mooring facilities would be provided at the mouth for visiting yachts. Mooring pontoons elsewhere in the Creek would provide a second safe access. The river walls would be repaired and treated to maximise visual improvement. The Creek bed would be cleared of debris.

navigation and boat usage

The Creek as a commercial resource with users including commercial shipping, house-boat owners and water-based leisure activities. Maximise navigability of the waterway to encourage full usage of the Creek as a port. This approach would benefit the business community and the small number of users who have house-boats or other reason to visit the Creek by boat. The existing flora and fauna would be substantially disturbed.

Proposals would include a maximum number of mooring facilities including a house-boat zone. Existing commercial wharves would be encouraged and others opened up where possible. The mouth and parts of the upper Creek would be dredged. A boat service pontoon and mooring facilities would be provided at the mouth for visiting yachts. Boat building and repair facilities would be located at the southern end of the Creek. The Creek bed would be cleared of debris. Repair and rebuilding of the river walls would aim to provide mooring facilities and working wharves.

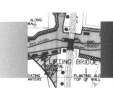

combination themes

In their pure form these uses were not viable on their own because they do not meet the needs of all the user groups. Although parts of each proposal were mutually incompatible, the future usage of the Creek was envisaged as a mixture of the three. "The challenge for the Creek Environment Project is to develop a strategy which allows all of the usages to flourish side by side. This will depend on the availability of land, the amenability of existing users to allow changes of emphasis to affect their properties and usage patterns, and on the overall vision of the local community." The report proposed enhancements consistent with each of the uses and one possible mixed use pattern. Discussions continue as to the relative merits of each theme and their potential combination.

Conserve & enhance

In this section we look at what is being done to protect the legacy and wildlife of the Creek, and at the approaches to conservation and enhancement which have arisen through the survey work described earlier in this book.

For those interested in the legacy, there have been some acute disappointments in the surrounding area – the destruction of important local buildings, views, and park space through the extension of the Docklands Light Railway, the unnecessary realignment of the ancient Crossfield Street, and the loss of the Wood Wharf barge repair yard after more than two centuries of continuous use. With just nine months left to fulfil the Fairview planning agreement over the future of the Landing Stage, the sole survivor of the world's first power station remains under threat. The restoration of Mumford's Mill – a key element in the Creekside SRB bid – has been removed from the programme due to high funding needs and a lack of clarity among potential developers. We have had to resign ourselves to the need for replacement of some of the oldest and most interesting river walls for flood defence purposes.

Despite these concerns there is a sense of cautious optimism, especially for Deptford High Street whose splendid 'in your face' medley of vernacular architecture has, at last, been recognised at a national level. When the Ha'penny Hatch route is finally implemented it will draw attention to the largest listed structure in the area – the 1836 railway viaduct. The proposals being developed for child-centred activities in the Rachel McMillan Building make that crucial link between physical and cultural heritage, and show how an understanding of the past can inspire renewal which meets contemporary needs.

a legacy of great character and vulnerability

Jonathan Ducker

The primary aim of the Creek Environment Project is to conserve the ecological value of the Creek and to create more opportunities to enhance its biodiversity. The habitat schemes outlined in this section will create conditions where wildlife can colonise. The methods might initially seem unorthodox but are designed to increase and sustain the wild populations of the Creek. The approach taken is based on a clear understanding of the power of natural colonisation, amply demonstrated by the story of the DLR bund described below. The proposed habitat schemes mirror the effects of industrial decline and neglect by creating artificial 'nooks and crannies' similar to those which arise through deterioration but without the flood defence implications.

cranes of Creekside

The remaining features of the Creek's industrial history have survived because of neglect and lack of development pressure from the 1960s to the early 1990s. Three significant brick structures – the London and Greenwich Railway Viaduct, Mumford's Mill and the Deptford Sewage Pumping Station (including the cast iron coal store canopies) – are protected as Grade II listed buildings.

By contrast the other identifiable grouping of relics, the wharf-side cranes, have suffered badly, with over half of those which remained in 1990 now lost. The last three cranes are now under threat of being scrapped, further sterilising Creekside's townscape and compromising its unique riparian identity.

The most obvious example is Prior's working crane to the immediate south of Creek Bridge, used on a daily basis to unload sand and gravel. As well as its visible operational use, it provides a strong upstand feature marking the gateway into Deptford Creek as well as into Greenwich from the west and into Deptford from the east. The intensive redevelopment proposals for the Norman Road wharves do not even consider retention and reuse of this locally-cherished and important feature of Creekside.

A second crane is located in the yard of Arts in Perpetuity Trust (APT) at Harold's Wharf. It complements the attractive red brick facia of the wharf's main building as well as the new DLR viaduct which sweeps past close by. Early plans are expected to be amended to ensure retention and reuse of the crane for performances and exhibitions.

The third crane is much smaller and is on tyred wheels. For over 20 years it served the Pope & Bond barge-builders at Wood Wharf. It is now at Dreadnought Wharf and is thought to be owned by a commercial tenant who will shortly vacate to make way for the cruise liner terminal and associated developments.

These cranes take a relatively small waterside footprint and were designed not to obstruct movement around and underneath their legs by vehicles and pedestrians. They could be retained as features of new developments and used for corporate advertising or public information, for mounting lighting, CCTV cameras or for sculptures. They offer so much more to the public than a scattering of irrelevant canons and anchors found along the frontage of so many Docklands developments. However, the reluctance of developers and landowners to consider retention and integration suggests that protecting the few remaining examples requires an urgent programme of listing applications to English Heritage. This would at least enable a proper consideration of the value of these irreplaceable artefacts.

a lost crane of Creekside on the Landing Stage

Richard Walker

Making these decisions and coming up with plans has been a long process. Through the ecology meetings, the Creekside Environment Open Meetings and with the support and advice of the Environment Agency and the Port of London Authority, plans are taking shape which take full account of all the survey work. None of the surveys stand alone and their findings must be considered in the context of the whole ecosystem. If you create a fish nursery to give shelter to flounder fry, be aware you are also providing a well-stocked larder for the herons and kingfishers.

natural colonisation

It comes as a surprise to most people that London is probably the most florally diverse area of its size in Britain. London's flora is highly dynamic and capable of colonising new areas rapidly, even those which seem most inhospitable. When you next meander down Deptford High Street look up; there is a variety of flora growing out of the canyon walls. Or take a look at the nearest piece of wasteland. Despite the evidence of wildflowers' capabilities all around us, when it comes to habitat 'creation' this is ignored. A mixture of 'wild' flowers are planted that in many cases do not occur in the location anymore, if they ever did. The many ramifications of this approach include:

- Planting what are perceived to be wildflowers actually denies space to the real wild flora of an area. It is, in effect, gardening (control of nature). It gives no value or respect to wild plants.
- Planting an ill thought out pick and mix of native species further erodes local distinctiveness. Most of what is built these days could be built anywhere and often is. One of the few features of the urban environment that remains locally distinctive is its wild flora and fauna. Habitat creation often creates meaningless landscapes.

It is astonishing how difficult it is to put across the concept of wildflowers actually being wild. Like butterflies, beetles, birds and mammals; grasses, herbs, shrubs and trees are as wild as tigers.

The approach being adopted at Deptford Creek is not to create habitats but to establish the right conditions for plants and animals to colonise, in the full knowledge that they will. There are two adjacent areas in the Creek where this approach is being taken. Ideas for the river walls can be found later in this section. But first, by good fortune, the capabilities of our local wild flora have been amply demonstrated, should demonstration be needed, during the construction of the Docklands Light Railway extension (DLR).

Nick Bertrand

natural colonisation on the DLR bund

the DLR bund
The building of the DLR viaduct across the Theatre Arm of the Creek necessitated the construction of a bund, to buttress the northern Creek wall. This artificial mound occupied about half the width of the Creek and was constructed of crushed concrete varying in size from dust particles to boulders up to 600 mm across. On top of this was a close-woven plastic sheet on which a further layer of crushed concrete was placed. The bank sloped into the Creek at an angle of approximately 55 degrees, shallowing out at the base. The process was completed in June 1997. No thought was given to what was happening to the bund until 31st May 1998 when, while

conducting a guided walk down the Creek at low tide, it was noticed that the bund had burst into flower. Mowlem, the DLR contractor, were contacted and access arranged to survey the flora and invertebrate fauna that had colonised. These surveys by **Conservation Works** and **Richard Jones** took place in early June 1998.

The bund had not been left alone in the intervening period. Some excess soil on the landward site had been tipped onto it and at times concrete left over from a pour was discharged onto it. The latter, in particular, had an impact on the colonisation possibilities of the bund, creating an impervious membrane over some of the middle and much of the upper parts. Across the rest, plants had made hay. In the space of a year the bund had been colonised by at least 68 species of plant. There were more species present – some are bound to have been overlooked while others were too juvenile to identify. This is 33% more species than occur in the next best Creek compartment (Hilton's Wharf) and includes 16 species new to the Creek. These are mostly opportunists common in the area such as redshank, scented mayweed, black medick, annual mercury, knotgrass and hedge mustard. Many of these were growing above high tide but it is remarkable how many species were tolerating total immersion twice a day from tidal action. These include species normally considered landlubbers such as common field-speedwell, Oxford ragwort, hawkweed ox-tongue, common chickweed, ribbed melilot, beaked hawk's-beard, spear thistle, mugwort, Guernsey fleabane and black horehound.

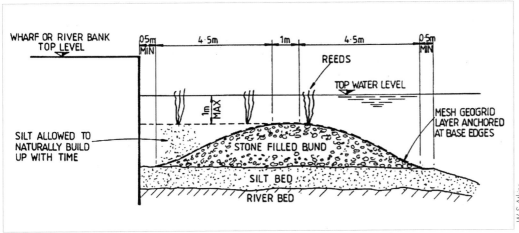

an early suggestion for environmental enhancement used an artificial stone filled bund

All the Creek's common wetland species had colonised, particularly the lower third of the bund: garden angelica, hemlock water-dropwort, clustered dock, celery-leaved buttercup, marsh yellow-cress and gipsywort. Less common species in the Creek, such as pendulous sedge and great willowherb, and two species associated with the mudflats rather than the walls, common water-starwort and water-pepper, had also colonised. Two new species for the Creek were watercress and hoary willowherb. Overall the bund had become the most 'natural' riverine feature within the Creek, containing a high diversity of plants which, in most cases, were growing in greater abundance than anywhere else in the Creek.

Invertebrate colonisation is not as rapid. The 1998 survey by Richard Jones found only a few invertebrate species. This is not surprising. Plant colonisation is quick and dramatic from wind- and water-borne seeds that then grow and mature. Plants are rooted to the spot and easily found. With invertebrates it is the adult stage of the life cycle that disperses and arrives on new sites often as singletons, small and secretive, and hence extremely difficult to locate until a population builds up. However, several species new to the Creek were found. Three species of ground beetle, *Bembidion* species, were found to be relatively common on the bund. One is common in the Creek, one had only been located once before and one was new to the Creek. Despite the paucity of species found, those that were discovered already characterised a more typical riverside community than occurs elsewhere in the Creek.

The bund was removed from the Creek in September 1998. In its short life it demonstrated that the major factor influencing the diversity and abundance of flora, and eventually fauna, in the Creek is the availability of habitat. It also highlights how hostile conditions are for plants in the walled Creek. In the space of a year the bund had become the single most diverse area in the Creek for plant life.

British Gas Transco site

Natural colonisation is not only rapid in rivers, when given the opportunity, but also on land. An opportunity for demonstrating this within the Creekside area has also been presented to us.

Nick Berrand

once the tarmac is stripped out, nature will return

Shortly after the start of the SRB programme, Lewisham Council and the Lewisham Group of the London Wildlife Trust entered into an agreement with British Gas Transco to manage their site on Creekside. This is the only piece of land adjacent to the Creek that cannot be built on due to the pipework running underneath. It has to remain operational so that emergency works can be carried out. The site was in the process of being completely scrubbed over, principally by buddleja, and necessary management works to prevent further encroachment of the tall herb and grassland communities were undertaken. Everyone involved in the future of the site was shocked to hear soon after the agreement that the DLR construction would involve turning this site into a temporary car park for Faircharm Industrial Estate. All the consultation had occurred some six years earlier.

The Lewisham Group of the London Wildlife Trust and local residents tried to have the car park relocated. This failed but DLR did agree to reconsider the design of the car park as long as no car parking spaces were lost. Transco minimised the amount of space on the site needed for operational reasons and just under a third of the site was saved from tarmac.

The two thirds of the site now under tarmac is due to be stripped in the spring of 1999. Following this removal, natural colonisation will be allowed to take place. Design will not be imposed on the site; instead design will be in response to the natural dynamic of what happens. Monitoring and management are the fundamental issues that are often neglected in habitat creation. There needs to be feedback between monitoring and management to arrive at a site with a mix of tall herb, grassland and scrub communities. In recognition of this the Lewisham Group of the London Wildlife Trust and the University of Greenwich have worked on an MSc Environmental Studies thesis project to produce a management and monitoring plan that will run throughout the recolonisation period.

This may appear an unusual approach to take yet it is the only way to take full account of the panoply of wild species that occupy this or any other area. Wild flora and fauna are more than capable of colonising new found land. It is confidently predicted that somewhere between 75 and 90 species of wildflower will colonise within the first year.

British Gas Transco Inlet

This is one of the few areas in the Creek where it is possible to establish a beach. It is proposed partly to infill and partly to retreat the flood defence in this area so that the amount of water storage volume of the Creek is not diminished. Natural colonisation will be allowed to take place and monitored. It is unlikely that it will become as diverse as the bund because the area is much smaller.

However, it will provide a valuable sloped or terraced haven for nesting birds, particularly swans, coots, moorhens and mallards. The site is very secluded and also benefits from the reflected heat of the sun's rays from the brickwork of the railway viaduct. Clearance of buddleia from the walls will increase the light. It will be within view of the Ha'penny Hatch bridge but restrictions on direct access to the site will ensure protection and privacy.

Transco beach

habitat enhancements

The ecological surveys have provided a basic understanding of the habitat requirements of the flora and fauna of the Creek. This knowledge has been pooled during regular ecology meetings over the past two years in order to find ways to conserve this unique wildlife. A number of ideas have emerged to enhance the habitats and thus appease the severe setbacks due to development. Several constraints limit the implementation of these ideas including: cost, maintenance, encroachment (relating to flooding concerns), obtaining permissions, and consideration for other uses of the Creek particularly for navigation.

rubbish substitutes

Whilst by no means all the rubbish in the Creek is made up of shopping trolleys, they are the most obvious objects abandoned in the watercourse and they obviously want removing. However, what appeared to be a simple task of 'Cleaning up the Creek' has evolved into a much more complex discussion. Rubbish is viewed differently by different people. However ugly the trolleys and their resulting shoals of silt and dead organic matter, they afford an excellent breeding and feeding habitat for many species. The mounds and the pools of water trapped between them at low tide provide hiding places for fish and foraging areas for birds. The flounder fry which nursery in the Creek for the first two years of their lives take off downstream and become the basis for a commercial fishing industry at Lea on Sea. Most people find this rubbish unsightly, though the sight of a kingfisher perched on a shopping trolley may change this perception. How we remove and deal with the 'rubbish', the precise technology of altering the Creek landscape, needs to be given serious thought.

The design of boat-friendly substitutes for shopping trolleys (without hard or jagged edges) made of willow baskets or similar materials is being considered. The baskets will no longer be a threat to small boats and will look more attractive than the trolleys. They will also serve to lock up the silt creating mounds. Hurdles of willow can be stapled to the river bed to create spaces similar to the old doors and corrugated iron dumped in the Creek. Under these, eels will thrive.

One section of the Creek in zone B5 is being used as a initial laboratory experiment. The trolleys here will be removed and replaced with wicker work. The hydrological effect of the replacement can be monitored without effecting any other part of the Creek. At the same

time the contracts have been let for the removal of the Large Single Objects in the downstream areas as far as the Creek mouth. Contractors will be required to demonstrate how they intend to remove these and the method showing the most sustainability and least environmental damage will be used.

Another suggestion is to have piles of hardcore (rubble) positioned in a tail extending downstream from the Lewisham College island. Porous materials such as brick would provide new micro-habitats for algae. Technically this would be encroachment (by

one of the Creek's Large Single Objects!

displacement of water). A better suggestion involves the demolition of the end of the island to make a gradual slope of rubble down to the Creek bed. This would avoid encroachment as material removed from higher up would offset the water displacement below. Unfortunately cost and permission factors are likely to exclude this ecological enhancement. But all is not lost, since the British Gas Transco inlet further downstream will include a gradual slope with terracing offering a haven for natural colonisation by plants and animals.

fishing perches and bird rafts

Marking posts to guide boat users clear of shallows or hidden hazards could incorporate side projections for use as fishing perches by kingfishers in addition to those provided by the timbers, ladders and vegetation of the Creek walls.

The extremes in tidal levels caused by the vertical walls of the Creek make successful nesting very difficult for water birds. Moorhens, coots and swans spend hours carefully collecting twigs to build on what they instinctively think is high enough ground or a sufficiently anchored floating nest, only to have their painstaking efforts washed away at the next tide. "Aren't birds stupid?" some might say; others might respond "aren't birds just like people? People build houses on flood plains!", but of course we humans are superior, our stupidity is proven and documented by historians, engineers and journalists!

Elaborate floating islands have been designed to provide viable nesting and roosting opportunities for water birds, but cheap and simple methods are the best. Some success has been achieved on the River Wandle using polystyrene-filled wooden pallets, which were adopted as nest sites by coots and great-crested grebes. These rafts proved to have been inadequately secured, however, and an armada of coot and grebe vessels was last seen heading for France – *quelle dommage!* In addition to the problem of adequate securing, in Deptford Creek two other conditions must be met. First, the Creek bed must be level where nesting rafts are secured otherwise eggs might well become scrambled eggs when the tide goes out! Secondly, the rafts and their securing attachments must not obstruct boat users. **Mike Canty** and **Jonathan Ducker** have surveyed the Creek and mapped suitable locations for nesting rafts (and therefore also for smaller waterfowl). It is hoped that the first nesting rafts will be installed in time for the 1999 nesting season as a trial.

kingfisher/sandmartin nests

Kingfishers may nest in the Creek if suitable sites are provided. Kingfishers normally tunnel for up to 1.5m into steep or vertical river banks to nest, usually from 75cm to 2m above normal water level. Such banks are only possible above the statutory flood defence height, but designs to simulate these conditions have been successful elsewhere. Pipes of 1.5m length can be incorporated into new walls at right-angles but slightly sloping down towards the wall face to prevent water entering. The far ends must be blocked so as not to interfere with flood defence functions. Some sand or clay soil can partially fill the pipe. Perches nearby may encourage birds to nest. The British Gas site, a proposed mini nature reserve, may be the place to install kingfisher nesting pipes. Similar designs might be employed to encourage sandmartins (summer visitors occasionally seen flying over the Creek). This would require vertical faced banks of at least 5m in length with several rows of spaced holes to encourage these colonial birds to nest.

nest boxes

In an ideal world (for all living things) such artificial structures as nest boxes would be superfluous. However, in the real world certain species might benefit from purpose-built and appropriately-sited nest boxes. The underside of the new DLR viaduct may be a potential place to attach swift nest boxes and maybe one or two kestrel nest boxes. Swifts nest in the vicinity but only a few buildings provide suitable conditions for their nesting. Kestrels currently nest in Mumford's Mill but should it become inhospitable to them after refurbishment it would be prudent to have provided alternative nesting sites. It is to be hoped that the provision of nooks and crannies in the structure of the new flood defence walls will make opportunities for grey wagtails to nest, but additional open-plan nest boxes could be attractive to both grey and pied wagtails and even black redstarts. The wooden fence noise barriers on the sides of the DLR track might be suitable for the attachment of wagtail nest boxes, though they would be rather exposed to kestrel predation.

terrestrial habitat

The semi-derelict industrial wasteland habitat adjoining the Creek has been home to a fascinating and unique plant and invertebrate community, the rare black redstart and the nationally threatened linnet. In view of the loss to development of major areas of this habitat on both sides of the Creek mouth, the priority for enhancement must be to provide the structural substrate conditions (beds of gravel/shingle/aggregate) to allow natural colonisation by vegetation and thus new pockets of suitable habitat for black redstarts and their like. This habitat can be at ground level or on flat roofs.

For terrestrial habitats along the Creek it is necessary to have a dialogue with each individual property owner concerned; some are co-operative, others consider any attempt at dialogue a threat to their profit margins. The Laban Centre have agreed to habitat enhancements on the flat roof of their planned new building. It has taken many months to convince Fairview New Homes plc of the habitat value of rubble and scrub. Unfortunately plans for the waterfront path and cycle route were too far advanced to incorporate the best option: open gravel habitat strips at the water's edge, with low screens to separate them from the footpath and cycle route. Moreover, riverside paths do not have to stay hard up against the water's edge but can meander more naturally, leaving 'living room spaces' for the wild residents and incidentally, provide more visual interest for human visitors.

The story of the DLR bund has shown that natural colonisation and not planting is the way forward. If trees and shrubs must be planted in the Creek mouth area, these should be local varieties of species which provide nesting habitat for linnets such as hawthorn or gorse.

repairing the river walls

Eight frontages were identified by the Environment Agency as needing urgent attention to maintain the flood defence function. However, by that time both the Fairview proposals and those for Greenwich Reach 2000 were well advanced and it seemed they would wish to complete works long before the EA would be in a position to carry out flood defence works. In such a case the owner would carry out all necessary works at their own cost, although

Land Drainage Consent would be needed from the EA. This is granted only if both technical and environmental aspects are acceptable.

Babtie undertook further investigations and feasibility designs for the other five priority frontages. The EA was looking for innovative solutions offering long-term integrity of flood defences, avoiding encroachment, and protecting and enhancing the environment.

Fairview New Homes plc

artist's impression of Fairview frontage, 2.12.96

For the majority of Deptford Creek frontages any new defences have be along the existing line of the frontage, either behind the existing retaining wall or narrowly terraced. The options that the EA would like to use, such as sloping earth banks, gentle terracing, or a retreated line of defence (negative encroachment!) are rarely possible in a congested area such as the Creek.

New frontage works must not only defend against flooding but fulfil a retaining wall function as well and it is this element which causes the majority of the cost. For many years anchored steel sheet piles have been used. A new wall was driven just in front of the old wall, anchors and ties installed, the gap between old and new walls backfilled, and a barren new steel face to the river created. This gave the riparian owner the cheapest new wall, and some new land into the bargain! The fact that the creek or river was being constantly narrowed and more of the valuable foreshore lost was apparently not a concern.

If steel piles are used timber cladding can make them more environmentally acceptable and encroachment can be kept to a minimum by careful design and construction. Many of the old walls comprise timber king piles spanned with horizontal planks. Here new king piles can be driven between the old ones and new planks inserted, limiting encroachment to little more than the thickness of the planks. Unfortunately it is difficult to use timber king piles now that design standards (and loadings) have increased. High quality hardwood also raises concerns about sustainable forestry. Instead steel H-piles can be used and these can be timber-clad to simulate (to the casual human observer, if not the wood louse) a timber king pile.

A variety of solutions have been proposed for the Deptford Creek frontages. One proposal is to provide a new steel sheet pile wall about 2 m behind the existing frontage, which will then be allowed to continue its physical deterioration while providing an excellent range of habitats. In due course when the new wall becomes exposed it can be clad with timber as appropriate. At another site the EA proposes that the existing frontage wall be replaced by a lower one and the flood defence wall sited a few metres landward as a separate structure on old crane rail foundations. The new frontage will be formed from steel H-piles and timber planks. Perhaps the site with the greatest opportunities is the Transco inlet, where a gradually sloping beach will be formed from the existing Creek bed to the required flood defence level. At other sites vertical frontages to allow for wharfage are being considered, but vertical walls constructed in front of raked walls involve excessive encroachment.

For all the works there is a great deal of consultation between the EA's internal experts (fisheries, ecology, marine biology, landscape, recreation and engineers) and with English Heritage, English Nature, Creekside Environment Open Meetings and others ensures the EA has the views of all parties. Last but far from least are the landowners themselves, who will have a new flood defence wall but must contribute a proportion of the cost of the works. Acceptable designs for new river walls tend to cost around £6,000 per linear metre.

river wall designs

Within the constraints and opportunities for river wall repair explored above, the Creek Environment Project had the task of designing enhancements to the walls to add value to whatever the EA was able to achieve in the course of their flood defence repairs.

Deptford Creek will never return to an open tributary with gently sloping natural banks. The project accepted this reality and designed the enhancements to work within the constraints of the vertical 'cliff face' presented by the Creek walls. The first step was to find out why the walls that were already providing ledges of greenery and nooks and crannies for invertebrates and birds were doing so, through the detailed surveys described earlier. Those surveys also generated ideas to protect and enhance those habitats and highlighted the importance of monitoring development impact in the future.

It was logical to expand what already existed into additional habitats, in particular on those sheet piled walls and engineering brick frontages that supported very little apart from algae. The ledges, nooks and crannies, provided by the old wooden fenders and the wooden walkways for access to loading and unloading boats, stood out as one of the most productive features of the Creek environment.

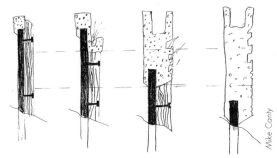

options for creating 'nooks and crannies' on new fenders

After much discussion and many initial sketches, it was agreed to design new vertical fendering with large 14"x14" recycled timbers kindly supplied by the Port of London Authority, with horizontal timbers at different heights above the mean neap high water level. These horizontal timbers will perform their original function of preventing boats from becoming trapped underneath them by being placed at an angle but will also offer new silt-trapping ledges to encourage plant colonisation.

It is intended to place the angled ledges at different heights in some places to establish which height is the most successful for colonisation and to enable a diversity of habitats. These ledges will also allow the incorporation of old timbers from existing walls in the Creek that are to be replaced. These will aid recolonisation of the new structures, though consideration must be given to the height and aspect of their existing position and the new position where they are relocated. The fixings of these timbers are currently being investigated by engineering consultants to arrive at a design that limits the build-up of damp and subsequent rot where the wood meets the river wall. Safety chains and ladders for safe exit as well as safe access will also be incorporated. Costings for future maintenance will also be assessed.

Enhancement is a slow process but, once physical structures like ledges, nooks, crannies, perches and nest sites are in place, it will be ongoing through nature's relentless energy and adaptability. It will be important to monitor what colonises, where and how, so that future developments can be enhanced along continually flexible lines to fit each section of the Creek as it becomes necessary.

management

There has never been a concerted, ecologically aware attempt to cleanse the Creek. The work is arduous, filthy and complex. Discussions are still ongoing about how to replace the offending rubbish with satisfactory substitutes so as to retain the habitats. Any archeological remains must be protected and any finds reported to English Heritage. Nevertheless, a start has been made.

Removing the rubbish is, however, only the beginning. Unless steps are taken to promote long-term custodianship, the reversal of all this good work could take only a matter of a few years or even months. Heavy rainfall will inevitably carry more rubbish from upstream into the Creek.

Rubbish-catching cages, higher fencing at dumping points, regular clean-up days and the need for a maintenance fund have all been discussed. Some ideas have worried our Environment Agency partners – cages in the channel can become clogged with rubbish in a few hours and cause flooding upstream by making the water back up in times of heavy rain. Higher fencing increases the isolation of visitors from the water and reduces safety: if you cannot get in, you cannot get out.

As with all regeneration programmes, an exit strategy must be planned as staff move on to other projects and the day to day management role comes to an end. The management of any site calls for an organisational structure that will co-ordinate and maintain the care, interest and involvement of local people, local authorities, visitors and statutory bodies. It would be possible to draw up a Stewardship Plan which included an advisory code of the Dos and Don'ts of Deptford Creek. This would similar to the Countryside Code. Only some elements would be legally enforceable, but overall it would promote wider understanding of responsible conduct.

constraints

The sites either side of the Creek will continue to change hands over the years and it is therefore crucial that the local authority planning departments play their part by recognising the importance of the Creek at an early stage in negotiations with landowners and prospective developers.

Planning gain (Section 106) agreements whereby developers agree to implement or contribute to the implementation of schemes which benefit the local area, could include a contribution towards the councils' liabilities for the future maintenance of a resource that complements the land and raises its value. This would support the statutory role of the Port of London Authority to remove rubbish that is a navigational hazard and that of the Environment Agency to prevent flood defence risks.

Architectural design of new riverside buildings can provide new habitats and managed access and views of the Creek if discussions are started early enough, often at no extra cost and sometimes even offering a cost-saving to the developer. Management of such features could be agreed at the design stage and be incorporated into private site maintenance schedules by the developer.

The enhancements to the river walls, including safety chains and ladders, will require a river works licence from the Port of London Authority and this includes a responsibility for future maintenance of these specific enhancements. These licences are not transferable when the landowner sells to another and it is therefore necessary to name the local authority as the licensee to ensure continuity. The PLA are currently requesting all councils with river frontages on the Thames and its tributaries to fund safety ladders and chains and their maintenance, to reduce the number of fatal accidents through drowning. They are therefore pleased to see the use of regeneration funds to put these features in place.

Legal agreements between the local authority and the landowner need to be drawn up to ensure agreement as to which party is responsible for each structure. An assessment of the likely maintenance cost to the councils in the future will need to be approved by committees before any construction work is commissioned.

The Creekside Environment Open Meetings will continue to be co-ordinated by the Floating Education Centre once the Environment Project and the Groundwork SRB are complete. This will ensure that maintenance can be assisted through a regular forum of communication and can be kept under regular review. This would allow a 'little and often' programme of works to be agreed and recommended to the budget-holders to keep major replacement costs to a minimum.

The educational aspect of the Creek will play a major role in future management by promoting awareness in local schools and among the general public of the need to look after such a dynamic site. It will also assist in recruiting interested people to help plan and take part in maintenance work. The Centre will be used to store equipment and boats and provide precious access to the Creek bed for staff and volunteers on workdays.

It is pointless cleaning up Deptford Creek if rubbish and pollutants are still thrown in further upstream. Lewisham Council is working with the Environment Agency, park user groups, Lewisham Town Centre supermarkets, Thames 21 (formerly Thames Clean) and other

interested groups and individuals to try to establish a system of river care in the future. The supermarkets were invited to send representatives to a meeting in autumn 1997. Store managers from Sainsbury and Tesco attended. They have experimented with methods of preventing shopping trolley loss, including higher fencing, wheel-locking sensors at store exits and van collections from local streets. Tesco are assessing the financial loss and whether it warrants paid collection. The trolleys are priced at £100–£500 each, according to size. Another local supermarket has installed rubber grid surfacing which makes trolley removal impossible.

The main conclusion of this meeting was that a co-ordinated approach is necessary between the supermarkets, the Environment Agency and local initiatives.

London Borough of Lewisham

volunteer on a Creek clean-up workday

education

The Creekside Floating Education and Visitor Centre is being developed with a working management group comprising: managers of other local environmental education centres, marine designers, local teachers and education advisers, local universities and colleges, the local group of the London Wildlife Trust, Environment Agency staff and the local manager for the Groundwork in Education programme.

This Centre will be designed to run on a low energy budget, with energy-saving light bulbs, insulation and a high efficiency gas combination hot water and heating system. Construction materials will be subject to the same scrutiny. This will provide a teaching subject in itself, leading to the question of human impact on the Creek itself and may help reduce environmental impact elsewhere in the local area through increased awareness.

The role of the Centre will be to promote the exploration and management of the Creek. It will be equipped to provide for all ages and levels of exploration from jam jars to microscopes, waders to computers, fishing nets to the internet. The new landing stage supporting the classroom will provide an outdoor space for summer lessons and a launching point for canoes and dinghies. Locating the classroom on the landing stage, only a few steps above the river bed, will bring the children into very immediate contact with the estuarine environment and, when the tide is in, will generate in visitors of all ages and abilities an intimate awareness of the very dynamic nature of the millions of tons of water which invade our capital city twice every day. Muddy Creek beds may be beyond the reach of wheelchairs, zimmer frames and pushchairs, but the Floating Centre is being designed to be fully accessible with a ramp which will accommodate the rise and fall of the tides.

At present, the public perceive the Creek as a dirty, smelly, polluted gully, incapable of supporting life. The older generation, remembering the river of their youth, believe that any contact with the water should be avoided. It is this attitude that we are working to change. We regularly take people into the Creek, on guided walks or when helping surveyors. Generally they have never walked along this watercourse or even been aware of its presence before. Most are astounded by the diversity of wildlife present and this is true not just for the public but also for specialists in various ecological fields. A 'nature study visit' no longer has to mean a coach trip to the countryside.

The Centre is being established as a company limited by guarantee and will be registered as a charity. It will be run by trustees selected by the present management group and will have a subscription membership to be known as the Friends of Deptford Creek. There will be local councillor and officer representation from both councils among the trustees but not in a majority role.

The trust will have the power to raise funds and seek sponsorship to sustain the Centre and its work. At present it is

an impromptu 'outdoor classroom' beside the Creek

Jill Goddard

unfunded by local authority budgets beyond the SRB programme to avoid competition with other environmental centres within the boroughs. The Centre will rely on sponsorship and charitable grants, alongside the money raised from visiting schools and local visitors, classes and guided walks and talks.

To consolidate this funding and promote local awareness, the project is working closely with the local Groundwork programme managers to ensure good communication of ideas and opportunities. The Groundwork in Education programme, part of the *Vital Centres & Green Links* SRB, has been running for two years. It has a strong focus on developing school grounds suitable for the 21st century, but has also transformed a derelict site into an educational herb garden and is currently working to create a Vital Centre for Primary Education in St Nicholas' Church. This centre, which is likely to be established by September 1999, will concentrate on the curriculum study of history, geography and other humanities. The experience developed here will be of great help to the Floating Education Centre, although the latter will also bring a strong scientific angle and will serve secondary as well as primary schools, and the general public.

idea sketch: Mike Canty

Facilities ashore & afloat.

The Floating Centre will hold copies of all the surveys relevant to the surrounding area. Future monitoring by schools, universities and wildlife groups will add to this baseline information, helping to monitor the impact of development on the Creek. This database will constantly reinforce the importance of a tidal creek to both boroughs and in the London-wide context and will help to protect an amenity through local use and awareness long after the one-off injection of Single Regeneration Budget capital has been expended.

While education centres are of great importance – not least in providing a focus for diverse activities – education can happen as part of everyday life around the Creek. Interpretation panels, leaflets, guided walks and talks can all help to raise interest and awareness. These offer a more informal approach which is particularly appropriate for adults who may feel intimidated by a classroom environment. Moreover, with imagination interpretation panels can fulfil several functions. For example, the panels in the Sue Godfrey Nature Park provide seating. One idea to discourage rubbish tipping is an interpretation panel on Deptford Bridge set an angle which will make it more difficult to throw objects over the parapet.

Deptford Discovery Team

interpretation panels doubling as seating

access

The Creekside Renewal Programme is sub-titled 'Building Bridges'. The Creek's obscurity has been a blessing for the wildlife but has led to a poor perception of it as more of a dirty drain than a valuable river. When people do get to enjoy the Creek at its best, whether wading along the channel or from a small boat, they are often overwhelmed by the presence of such an asset in the midst of the urban environment.

Improving public access is a core aim of the Creek Environment Project. A large-scale early survey on Land Use, Access and Recreation was commissioned from **Urban Initiatives**. This informed the consultation process from an urban design perspective but was of limited immediate value in decision-making. It is essential to understand the Creek's history and ecology before making specific proposals about access. The lessons of the surveys, the consultation and the work of the **Deptford Discovery Team** in developing local sustainable transport routes, have made us wary of any simplistic answers.

types of access

There are numerous types and degrees of access to be considered.

access to the water's edge – amenity

This kind of pedestrian access should offer 'peeps at the Creek' without causing disturbance to wildlife. In some places it may be desirable to incorporate a stretch of bankside walk, but it was recognised at an early stage that there were severe practical limitations as well as ecological concerns acting against a 'towpath' approach.

access across the Creek – obstacle

The one access project which had been established before the bid was written, was the reinstatement of the historic Ha'penny Hatch footbridge. The largest single capital item within the SRB programme, this project had been promoted by the Deptford Discovery Team, as part of a circular local network which offered a hub for the National Cycle Network and Thames Path and Cycle Route.

The footbridge, which spanned the Creek in two sections beside the railway viaduct at the very centre of Creekside, was built in 1836 and removed some time in the 1930s. The section over the main channel was a drawbridge to allow for navigation. Reinstatement of the bridge will reconnect the towns of Deptford and Greenwich and offer a safe, direct, healthy and pleasant alternative to the two trunk roads (A2 and A200) which are currently the only links.

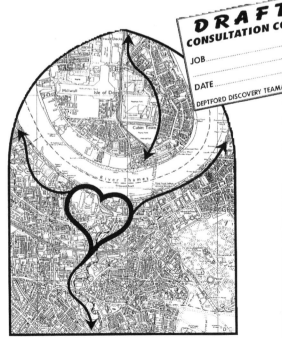

at the heart of the Thames Path & Cycle Route

Penny Metal

access to river use – leisure & residential

River uses of the Creek at high tide could include fishing, leisure craft such as dinghies and canoes, residential boats, industrial use of the kind currently undertaken by Prior's, and indeed access for surveying and monitoring. It is important to remember that the Creek cannot be safely used unless there are adequate points of 'egress'. At low tide the Creek could be accessible for educational visits and ecological monitoring.

mooring rings are few and far between

views – sense of identity, visibility of the Creek

To address the misperception of the Creek as a dirty drain involves education at all levels, from the formal classroom as part of the Education and Visitor Centre, through a programme of walks and boat trips, to the incidental 'education' of information panels, signs, leaflets and posters. The benefit of these will only be forthcoming if people can access views of the Creek. The DLR extension will enable views of the upper Creek never seen before, although the sound-proofing fences may inhibit this in some areas.

quiet space/haven

Those who know the Creek well love its sense of privacy and the soothing sound of the water. There are areas which are havens for wildlife and should remain so; there are other spaces, like the Booker's car park, which offer a quiet private space enjoyed by small groups of teenagers, anglers, and Sunday wanderers. These areas can be improved, not with expensive landscaping but through good maintenance and, possibly, interpretation panels.

Not all access has to be via a permanent public right of way. Indeed the promotion of responsible access requires a distinction between permissive routes which allow access by those in the know (or the intensely curious) and encouraged routes which are properly way-marked to welcome and manage visitors.

checklist for access planning

routes and bridges

does it provide a worthwhile link?

can it be made safe?

does it involve purchase/compensation?

will it put undue pressure on wildlife?

peeps at the Creek

does the land user have security concerns?

does the proposal protect wildlife?

is the space hospitable?

is the view interesting?

moorings

is there enough soft mud?

is the landowner amenable?

could services (electricity, water, sewage pump-out) be made available?

Graham Maxwell @ Othens

progress and constraints

Access is a complex issue which can only be viewed holistically. At any given moment within the planning process it can feel more like a jumble of ideas and aspirations, challenges and constraints, than any strategic overview. However, over time it is possible to steer the development process to achieve some of those proposals which emerge as priorities.

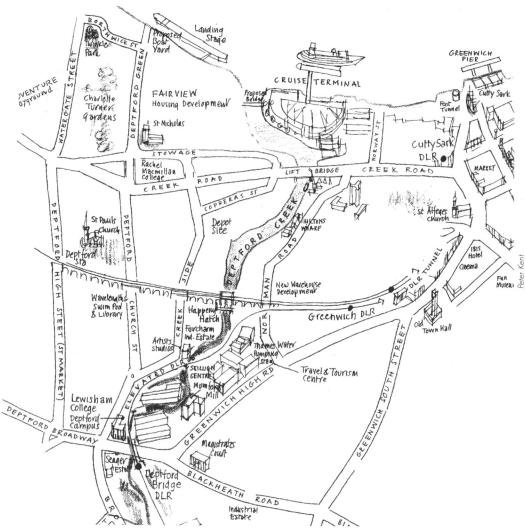

Theatre Arm

Currently used by Mowlem. Anticipated return to Peter Kingston. Excellent opportunities to develop access to the Creek and from the Creek to Deptford amenities. Julian Kingston has proposals for mooring/workshop facilities for his own boat & barge-building business. Land to the rear of pub could also provide permissive pedestrian access.

Deptford Bridge

Problem of concrete channel leading to the perception of the Creek as a drain/tip. Info panel on bridge, angle it to deter tipping. Could do something similar on Creek Road Bridge.

Lewisham College site

Unfortunately not enough funding to change the chain link fencing. Could put a gate in the fence with a ladder for maintenance, public walks, etc. Island provides a good viewing platform. Could link human access to the tides – get on at high tide, not at low (bird-feeding) tide, using a tidal indicator lock on the access bridge.

Art in Perpetuity Trust

Arts workshops with Creekside yard accessed via substantial gates. Use as outside workspace and material storage limits public access. Great views.

SOUTH ELEVATION OF LEWISHAM APPROACH   1:200   PROPOSED LIGHT FITTINGS EVERY TWO ARCHES

Thames Path

Current Thames Path ignores entire Deptford Waterfront. Proposal is for a 6m wide pedestrian/cycle frontage on the Fairview site, round the boatyard, along the Thames, step back to Stowage before Hoy Stairs. Expected habitat creation scheme on Crown Wharf frontage (rubble, restricted access). When will the path be accessible? Probably not till Fairview want highways within the site adopted by local authority (Oct 99?). Sculpture/bandstand at Creek mouth is important for identity. The path provides only physical access – who 'owns' the identity of the foreshore? This is why the Landing Stage is so important for Creek and boat access. Section 106 (planning gain) agreement – time running out for solutions to be found.

Creek Mouth Bridge

Land brokerage deal passed liability for the bridge-building to GR2000. Does the planning application include this bridge? If Clearwater don't do it as part of the cruise liner development it won't happen. In 1993 it was 5 yrs away, it's still 5 yrs away. Included in all plans but remains dependent on economic climate and determination of planning dept.

The Mid West

Development of the depot site will include access to frontage – possible river garden with café/terrace. Walls in this section are being repaired with new terrestrial habitat on wall top. This part of the Deptford bank is key to retaining black redstarts on the Creek. People coming in and out at Laban is ok and there is a good view but a path along the frontage would be very problematic.

Ha'penny Hatch

Critical link across the Creek, connecting Deptford and Greenwich. Especially useful if Education Centre can be based on Thames Water site. Project enjoys widespread popular support built up by Deptford Discovery Team. Frustration over delays which have caused some loss of originally envisaged elements (CCTV, waymarking and interpretation, safer road crossings at Creekside and Norman Rd). Expected to start on site in spring 1999.

Gordino's to Brookmarsh

No case for public access while it remains primary employment land. If it changes to residential (unlikely given current UDP zoning) there should be access within constraints of ecological needs.

Creek Road Bridge

Very unpleasant trunk road but lifting bridge still fascinates, and Prior's crane is a landmark feature. 'Gateway to Greenwich'. Sustrans can't get through Fairview site so concentrating on Creek Road Bridge.

Hoy Stairs

Owned by the pub: sympathetic but unwilling to explore options yet. Proposal to install mooring services (electricity, water, sewage pump-out) taking advantage of Fairview works on Crown Wharf. Access for local people to boats and boating life?

Norman Road Wharves

Planning application prior to site assembly. Uncertainty & lack of timescale. Seems to include substantial but partial Creek access for general public, as well as potential wharf use (live-work units). Current informal access through Hilton's car park. Potential Laban–Hilton's bridge: does planning application identify the bridge as possible or proposed? Should resolve other bridge problems before inventing new ones.

Faircharm

Long car park frontage with chain link fencing. Before DLR, access was quite relaxed. Young anglers used a gate in the fence: safety concerns. Potential for cheap permissive access by replacing fence with wall top railings, but Creekside SRB paid for new fencing as high and unattractive as the old.

Skillion's

No intention of moving. Happy to allow moorings through rental of office space.

Booker's

Supportive. Provided the only access to the Creek at low tide for surveying etc, but lease ends in less than 2 yrs. Check ownership with Land Registry. Try to keep responsible access. Low wall, good viewing/interpretation point. Young people use this site. Could break up some of the hard surfacing.

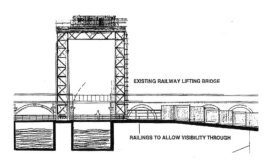

EXISTING RAILWAY LIFTING BRIDGE

RAILINGS TO ALLOW VISIBILITY THROUGH

issues and implications

There has been a gap between the importance attached to access in the original *Building Bridges* bid and the focus it has been given within the actual programme. This is partly understandable as the project leaders and officers involved began to realise the complexity of the issues involved. Those local authority officers who have responsibility for sustainable transport are used to a road-side context and do not necessarily grasp the subtlety of the Creekside situation.

route planning

When considering access issues, it is easy to draw lines on a map but implementing such routes is much more complex. One important consideration which is usually left till late in the process is the tangle of liabilities which exist or will be created once a route is implemented.

There are a plethora of authoritative bodies to negotiate with, including the Environment Agency (responsible for flood defence, ecological issues and access), the Port of London Authority (responsible for maintaining the navigational channel), the local authorities and the riparian landowners. Often, as in the Creekside example, the landowners are themselves large ex-public corporations such as Railtrack and Thames Water. It was a shame that these two were not invited to join the Creekside Partnership from the beginning. Almost all route planning needs to deal with ownership and compensation issues, which may include adapting leases to reflect the loss of use of a strip of land, compensatory works to party walls (or, in the Creekside case, railway arches) and addressing a range of security concerns.

Once the route is implemented it will have maintenance requirements. The most obvious approach for a public route is for the local authority/ies to adopt it as a 'highway'. An authority will usually have a scale of charges for such an adoption (which can be as much as 30% of the capital cost, but may be negotiable if the public benefit is obvious).

Given all these issues, it is clear that access routes must offer a critical mass of public worth to justify their cost. They will also need 'champions': even a comparatively short stretch of route can be extremely time-consuming and frustrating, and will only reach fruition with long-term intensive work. Such champions can come from the community sector (as in the case of the Ha'penny Hatch) or from within the local authority or agency. However, our experience is that while community-based promoters can achieve far wider public support, they must be given the full support of the agency (including financial assistance and officer time to help with legal and political issues) to ensure the project is embedded in the vision and implementation of the programme as a whole.

Waterlink Way

This was an early proposal from within Lewisham Council to create a north–south link from the Thames to Lewisham and beyond. The main consultation was during the last review of the Unitary Development Plan (1991) which, given the substantial work undertaken in the past three years, both on surveying the Creek's assets and on developing access proposals, is now extremely out of date. The project was recently brought before the Creekside SRB board and funding of £70,000 agreed. The lack of recent consultation has angered many local residents and businesses, especially because the funding must now be spent before 31st March 1999.

A number of elements of the proposal raise concerns about safety, while other sections appear to ignore opportunities to complement other projects. The lack of synergy between Waterlink Way and the Ha'penny Hatch route (currently being delivered by Greenwich Council) is indicative of the problem. Creekside the road is very dangerous and a width restriction at the railway bridge could protect users of both routes.

conclusions

surviving regeneration

Deptford Creek presents a jumble of cultural, historic, environmental and wildlife features. The studies commissioned by the Creek Environment Project, in partnership with other agencies, have demonstrated how a range of techniques can be used to assess the quality and character of these aspects of the Creek. By combining the studies it becomes apparent that these interests interrelate, indeed are often mutually dependent, and that future policy should address the processes which create and sustain key features.

At times the approach taken in this book, and in the many local meetings, may seem adversarial and full of conflict. Partnerships are undoubtedly key to regeneration, yet they are far from simple and the cosiness of the word hides the real dilemmas, divisions and disagreements at the heart of the renewal process. Nevertheless there has been a gradual sharing of perspective. The clearest example would be the consistent involvement of the Environment Agency in the Creekside Environment Open Meetings. This has led to an understanding of each other's concerns so that even the most fanatic historians and ecologists understand the necessity of flood defence repairs and will stand up against encroachment, even when to do so compromises projects we would like to see happen in Creekside. Meanwhile the EA have learned a great deal from the surveyors and other local people. Another example is the regular attendance of Mark Seaman from Mowlem, the contractor for the Docklands Light Railway Lewisham Extension, which crosses Deptford Creek in four places, shadowing, disturbing and disrupting the legacy and wildlife. Being properly informed of its progress is essential, and this is a two-way process which allows surveyors to inform and discuss with Mowlem, for example, the impact of construction of Creek usage and ecology.

The Creek Project has focused local activism and knowledge. The networks being developed are a successful form of capacity building which harnesses the enthusiasm and skills of individuals. The 'local profiles' at the end of this chapter, and the surveyors themselves, convey the excitement that many people feel once they can contribute their own ideas to the process of renewal planning, in whatever format.

The process of surveying and consultation has also caught the imagination of English Nature, the London Wildlife Trust and the Environment Agency. Elsewhere in inner London such national and regional organisations are seldom invited to become involved in the regeneration process on a local scale.

There is a strong sense of conservation on the agenda. The Director of LEED, a large and influential department within Lewisham Council, recently spoke publicly about "what we in the Council are calling regeneration through conservation". At the same event, the launch of the Royal Commission's local exhibition of their Deptford High Street study, a senior officer of the Commission described Deptford as "a remarkable place" where the buildings "are rare witnesses". He stressed that regeneration depends on understanding and valuing local distinctiveness and that heritage is not separate from everyday life but something in which the whole community has a stake. His statement that "the future of local heritage depends entirely on the interest, enthusiasm and motivation of local people" echoes the lessons we have learnt in Creekside.

why are we still concerned?

We are now at the next stage of the dynamic redevelopment of the area, one among many dramatic moments in the Creek's multi-millennial history. Sites are changing hands rapidly, a potentially positive situation which could increase both local input and land values, yet one that can be a dangerous force in a context where a strategic vision is still lacking. The reviews of the Unitary Development Plans in both Greenwich and Lewisham boroughs offer an opportunity to create detailed local planning and design guidance. Yet it sometimes appears that the tails are wagging the dogs if the reviews are reactive to developer interest rather than proactive in the interests of community regeneration and the protection of local assets. On the other hand, SRB managers are sometimes criticised by the private sector for paying "too much attention to community interests". Perhaps the Creekside Environment Open Meetings have supported a level of increased local participation which *expects* to make a difference.

the APT crane

Richard Walker

The Creekside Renewal programme lags behind in terms of strategy development, dissemination of information, network and partnership-building. This has led to frustrations at many levels of local life. One manifestation of this has been the New Creekside Initiative – a group of landowners, developers and consultants who submitted an outline bid asking for £5m more SRB funding for Creekside. Unfortunately this group appears to define 'stake-holding' exclusively in terms of land and property; the battle for wider ownership is far from won. A new Creekside Strategy is planned by the SRB programme in 1999. Attempts at urban design masterplanning to date have met with vehement local criticism because they failed to grasp the importance of the unique character and potential of Creekside. It is hoped that the new strategy will better reflect the findings of the surveys and the ethos of regeneration outlined in this book. Meanwhile, elsewhere in the local area bids are being prepared from within the community sector itself with a new approach based firmly on pre-renewal research undertaken by local residents themselves.

With the SRB programme coming to an end in just over two years, there are also concerns about the future. The Creek Environment Project has a built-in forward strategy, via the Education Centre, the Friends of Deptford Creek and the proposed Stewardship Plan. The surveys have revealed the additional knowledge and expertise which local planning authorities need in order to create planning briefs which can guide developers of all descriptions to take account of the ecological, amenity and heritage criteria already established. Such briefs should relate directly to the character, context and local value of each site and be based on a consensus reached through intensive consultation.

changing attitudes

Over the life of the project we have seen a change in perceptions of how development proposals can *include* nature conservation benefits. Gravel surfaces, sparse shrub planting and managed 'rough' areas of low-growing naturally colonised plants can provide food for black redstarts and a habitat for the local flora and fauna. These may be incorporated into both public and less public areas, industrial premises, roof tops and river frontages.

The key achievement is to encourage developers and planning departments to consider these options very early on, when the first site layout plans are discussed. If planning permission is sought without these factors being considered, time and money on all sides will be wasted through protracted alterations to plans and many valuable opportunities lost.

The Creek Environment Project aims to support the efforts made by developers in their site plans by promoting any such improvements as examples of good practice. There has also been a chance to demonstrate that conservation groups can help in designing new habitats and pointing out potential that had been previously been missed.

We await each new development with almost equal measures of concern and optimism. Perhaps this one will be different? Projects in the pipeline include the Laban Centre (a project favoured by Lewisham Council, the result of an international design competition and an Arts Lottery development grant) and Greenwich Reach 2000 (shops, flats, hotel, cruise liner terminal). Other newbuild proposals include the Caribbean Heritage Centre and the Contemporary African Arts Centre.

Integrated into the urban fabric...

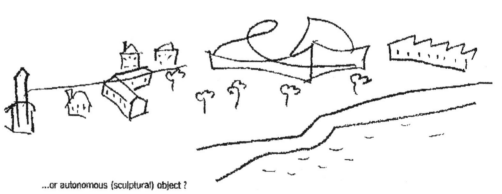

...or autonomous (sculptural) object ?

Laban Centre London (drawings by Herzog & de Meuron)

Perhaps it is only nostalgia to think that we can save the Creek, its life and legacy, from irresponsible 'renewal'? However, in line with the policy statements of every relevant level of government (central, local, European, global, quango), we will continue to argue for sustainable sensitive regeneration which respects and protects 'the genius of place'.

some Creekside regeneration stories

We have an opportunity to make a substantial difference to the lives and environment of the people of Creekside by supporting a mix of social, environmental and infrastructure projects which have popular support and a track record of success.

- the Vocational Guidance Project run by Milton Court Employment Resource Centre. Applauded by the independent evaluation team from Goldsmiths College, the project has an excellent reputation and has surpassed its 'outputs' (quantifiable measures of change set by Government Office for London).
- the McMillan Herb Garden was created on a derelict and fly-tipped space by Groundwork's local programme managers, the Deptford Discovery Team, as part of the 'vital centre' of Deptford Green. Other Groundwork projects in the area are:

the restoration of part of St Nicholas' churchyard including new celebration gates; a dramatic start to school grounds development at Rachel McMillan Nursery School with works to the entranceway including a musical safety barrier; and a grant to help establish the McMillan Legacy Group to progress proposals for the Rachel McMillan Training College, now assisted with a grant from the Creekside SRB.

- the Youth Action programme is working to involve local young people in sports, circus training and media skills. Residential trips to the outdoor centre at Macaroni Woods are arranged. The project offers an important source of informal advice and personal education.

- the Watergate Centre, Deptford's Community Boatyard, has succeeded, after many years of negotiations, in obtaining a land site on the Fairview development and attracting Tideway Sailability to run the sailing club. The project continues to be intricately linked to the future of the Landing Stage.

- *Revealing the Waterfront* was the title of a Millennium Lottery bid proposing the restoration of the Landing Stage as public open space. The complexity and timescale of the legal agreements delayed support for the bid. The bidding process included a visit from Simon Jenkins, chair of the Millennium Commission who, interestingly, believes that the Thames should be impounded. The final agreement with Fairview did include a 'stay of execution' for this important structure.

- the Deptford Adventure Playground in Prince Street is the only survivor of numerous such facilities which existed in the 1970s. Extremely popular with local young people all year round, the playground hosts an annual pyro-technics display for Bonfire Night and has also been used to stage classical plays performed by local theatre group, the Hush Hush Ensemble. The Adventure Playground has received funding through Creekside SRB for a building and a new sports pitch.

London Borough of Lewisham

local children at the Adventure Playground

lessons for good practice

There are some very important lessons to learn from the regeneration experience in Creekside. These range from issues of identity to the detail of outputs.

The identity of any regeneration scheme should be rooted in the local understanding of the area. The identity of Creekside has been problematic because the term is associated with Creekside the road. Historically 'Creekside' has tended to mean the Deptford banks and people living on the Greenwich side can feel alienated by this, assuming the programme has nothing to do with them. We have tried to counter this through door-to-door leaflet drops and alternating meetings between both sides but the representation from the west bank is still far stronger. This may relate to the far greater investment in community development within Deptford, and to the unique influence of 'tourist Greenwich' on the other side. Building a common identity will take many years.

Keeping project objectives flexible will allow for research-based decision-making. The Creek Project stated that 750 metres of river wall would be repaired, replaced or enhanced and public access improved, but did not say exactly where, which offered the chance to use the survey data and partnership advice once the project was running to select the right sites. Outputs can be far too optimistic when bids are written. With such a little known site, we decided to be realistic and conservative and have now been rewarded through the partnership process achieving and exceeding those targets in reality.

Dedicated staff time is essential to good partnership and salaries need to be built into the funding bid. A great deal of administration is involved as well as project development work and managing consultants, yet it is easy to underestimate how much staff time is required and mistakes will cause slippage during the life of the project. The Creek Project converted some of its original capital funding into revenue to enable a second member of staff to be employed once we realised our own mistake.

Those staff, whoever they are employed by, will be most effective if supported by a communication network that ensures that the local authorities and other bodies involved, know what is going on. Each agency needs the opportunity to tie services and potentially complementary projects together to maximise the benefits.

It is important to talk to as many people as possible when a bid is being put together and allow time to do so. This was partly recognised but should have gone on for longer. Setting up regular open meetings and communication channels right at the beginning of the project is essential. The recognition within new regeneration guidelines of the need for a set-up year is a welcome change. Those who attended public meetings took approximately two years to understand who does what, how the funding works and, most importantly, how to feel part of and work with the project. However much this was a formal project, officially run on a pre-planned timescale, we discovered that people need time to get to know each other. The partnership benefits from this project only really began to grow when we all decided that we could trust each other to have the same goals in mind. Of course, discussions will continue about different ways of reaching those goals – this is the way the best solutions are found.

This building of trust and awareness could probably have been helped by a community liaison worker for the SRB programme as a whole being in post from the start, assisting with the time-consuming but necessary work of explaining to local residents and local businesses the detail of the programme and how they could get involved. In general, it is local professionals who are able to provide the most detailed surveys and the best post-survey follow up monitoring and advice. Their commitment is immensely valuable.

The regeneration of a unique asset like Deptford Creek requires a clear, consulted vision and an agreed strategy for its implementation. Land use will continue to change after the regeneration project has ceased. This need not be problematic but guidelines need to be in place for new tenants and for developers to enable them to support the work already done. The local planning authority can play an important role in supporting environmental projects. Early consultation between developers and interested local groups can lead to environmentally beneficial designs before costly plans are drawn up. Where this has not happened, conflict and delay have been the result, to no-one's benefit.

Thorough survey work has revealed the inadequacies of some environmental impact assessments submitted by developers to planning departments. This is not just a local observation. Consultation is taking place nationally, led by English Nature, concerning which criteria should be incorporated into planning guidance to ensure a consistent standard is maintained.

Tendering to local authority approved lists has brought some conflict by excluding local people and businesses involved in the project's development. It is not always possible to join if the lists are 'full' or the requirements inappropriate. It has been suggested that looking at how contracts are let would be helpful where local labour and local involvement is encouraged.

For the Environment Agency the planning of flood defence works at Deptford Creek has been a template. Staff have spent time in consultation, both through attending the Environment Open Meetings and in detailed discussions with surveyors. If the EA as an institution has increased the value it places on local consultation, the Creek Project can be proud.

recognising river users

"What was a wonderful life in the 1960s and 70s got devastated in the 1980s by private companies taking over moorings." In 1985 Mike Canty came to Dreadnought Wharf. In the seven years he was there he had no lease. At Skillion's he rents an office space and is therefore slightly more secure, although the mooring itself is still unrecognised. The key issue, then, is the insecurity of boat owners.

If the Creek is to be successfully protected the needs and interests of boaters must be balanced with those of wildlife. The Creek's bridges create natural divisions between zones. It has been suggested that there should be free movement from the Thames to Creek Bridge, with the middle reaches constrained by the road bridge, and a much quieter space beyond the railway bridge.

boats in the Creek, with Pumping Station behind

Marie O'Connell

However, there is no authoritative body in a position to legislate, guide, enforce and manage such a situation at the local level. In Holland the canals are run by the town councils who license boats for an annual fee, inspect them regularly and provide certificates of inspection and number plates. This system, which is comparable to the treatment of motor vehicles in the UK, ensures a basic level of safety and regulation. The Port of London Authority is a historic institution which was established to run an industrial port, a remit that can no longer meet the diversity of river users' needs. When one Creek boatowner tried to pay mooring fees for the two rings in Theatre Arm he was told it was not worth the paperwork. It is said that other boats in the Creek have sunk, discharging oil into the water.

There is concern that the boating situation will become polarised between prestigious sites such as St Katherine's Dock which attract wealthier boatowners with well-kept vessels, and so-called 'backwaters' like Deptford Creek which may end up with the craft no-one else wants. As Mike puts it "every boat that has come into the Creek since the project began has just strolled in". This lack of coherent policy means that people who have lived on boats in the Creek for many years continue to suffer intense insecurity, and there is no way of enabling boaters to make use of the Creek with full consideration for ecology and amenity. As with ecological legislation and guidance, the law can only be effective if it is enforced at both a local and a strategic level. This is an obvious task for the new Greater London Assembly which could debate the issues, publish guidance for local authorities and, perhaps, establish an appropriate modern and publicly accountable body to play a proactive role in servicing the changing needs of river users.

This discussion highlights the inadequacies of the whole development process. Development proposal sketches regularly show boats yet make no provision for moorings, steps, ladders or services. The dumping of sewage waste directly into the Thames and its tributaries is becoming a serious concern, but boaters can only behave responsibly if the facilities are provided. Mike's proposals for boating services at Hoy Stairs have hit a snag because of Fairview's reaction to the concept of 'sewage pump-out'.

Hoy Stairs could encourage access for overnight moorings

Developers prefer a large, flat, cleared, self-contained site without complications, yet to achieve this destroys the local pattern of the ecological and historical landscape. Too often indigenous plants are removed from areas which are later to be 'landscaped', existing businesses are displaced from buildings which are zoned for business use and the industrial heritage is destroyed prior to replacement by 'traditional riverside crafts'. Since developers rarely have a long-term responsibility for their sites, it is essential for planners to take a more proactive approach. If boats are shown on plans, for example, planning officers could ask applicants for details of the facilities to be provided. Unfortunately, many planning departments in riparian boroughs lack expertise in relevant fields including ecology, archaeology and navigation issues.

celebrations

The Ralph Merryfield award
London and Middlesex Archeological Society (LAMAS) annual conference. March 1998

The award was created in memory of a well-respected authority on the archaeology of London. The Creek Environment Project was nominated for the award in recognition of its successful work in raising the profile of the archaeological and historical legacy of the Creekside area in partnership with English Heritage and Pre-Construct Archaeology's study of the power station site. LAMAS were also supportive of the project's intention to use the information from the surveys to inform the regeneration designs.

Presentation of a cheque was made at the LAMAS annual conference held at the Museum of London. This has helped towards this publication and the Museum of London have kindly offered to assist by stocking it in the museum bookshop.

River Calling
London Rivers Association Conference – September 1998

This conference focused on the significance of water space to the culture and life of London. Delegates included local authorities, MPs, statutory bodies, voluntary organisations, landscape design and marine engineering firms, and commercial businesses connected with the Thames, alongside international visitors from the Hudson River Foundation.

The development of a water space strategy was supported as policy advice required for the Greater London Assembly and to inform the Urban Task Force initiative for developing brownfield sites, many of which are adjacent to the river. The Creek Environment Project was asked to attend the conference with a display and leaflets on its work and many interested delegates asked questions.

Low Tide Walk
A public event , 31st May 1998

Having built up detailed knowledge and enthusiasm for the Creek among the surveyors, it was important to discover whether other local people would find the same fascination with this tidal waterway. We decided to organise a trial public walk.

one of the guided groups wading down the Creek

The project organised guides, Health and Safety advice sheets and First Aid, and 30 pairs of waders and sticks. The Environment Agency, the Lewisham Group of the London Wildlife Trust and all the other project volunteers and surveyors gave their support on the day with display materials, leaflets and volunteer guides.

We wondered how people would react to all that mud – would they complain that the fish were too small and too secretive? Would they say it was boring? Would we lose half of them if they got too excited and ran ahead and got stuck in a heavily silted bank? Nothing like that happened. We were overjoyed to see that once people start looking in shallow pools for fish and finding that the world has a completely different timescale when you have to take the tide into account, everyone relaxed into a childlike state of natural wonder. They wanted to know when the next walk would be held and we have been receiving expressions of regret ever since from those that missed it on the day. Best of all, no-one forgot the serious advice on safety. More walks are planned.

River Trip
Environment Agency – March 1998

When the EA organised and funded an informative trip on the Thames for Greenwich and Lewisham local authority staff, it was very different from the usual guided tour. The combined knowledge of the EA and the Museum of London archaelogical staff was fascinating. They pointed out archaelogical and historical features along the foreshore, new river walls and developments, and discussed the processes of design that had, or had not, worked, noting innovative approaches that could be used elsewhere.
The improvement in water quality and wildlife species using the Thames was explained. There is still a need for education to change the attitudes of those who still see it as dirty because of the silt-laden water colour. The Thames is now recognised as an international success story because of the clean-up of the pollution that led to it being classified as officially 'dead' in the 1970s. As the boat passed the entrance to the mouth of Deptford Creek, the EA commentator praised the efforts of the Creek Environment Project to add to this success story.

Planners from both local authorities expressed surprise at the range of design approaches and agreed that the trip had been extremely useful in increasing their understanding of river issues. Seeing the foreshore and its structures from the river is an important part of waterfront planning too often neglected. It is a constant irritation to boaters, for example, that planners "plan to the water's edge" without considering the river itself.

Recite Lotus 2000 Transnational European Initiative
Thames Gateway Partnership

The Thames Gateway Partnership covers the area on either side of the River Thames, from the Lewisham frontage as far as Gravesend and the estuary mouth. It comprises twelve London boroughs and aims to promote the regeneration and inward investment potential of an area that has suffered industrial decline.

The Recite programme is a well respected European initiative that recognises the international relevance of this aim and the value of sharing experience in London with partners in other countries. One of its main aims is to find ways to ensure that local communities benefit from the regeneration programmes of the future. It is also seeking to share methods of promoting local employment opportunities and sustainable development policies. The three year funding, starting in April 1999, is to be spent on exchange visits to the pilot projects, research on current practice and the sharing of information which will eventually change policy within partner countries. International partners so far are Aspropyrgos in Athens, Palermo in Sicily and Leipzig in Germany.

The Deptford Creek project is working with the Thames Gateway team to demonstrate the achievements of the project to date and develop ways in which information may be shared. It is hoped that finances will be available to translate this book and provide internet information and updates for international partners. The Floating Education and Visitor Centre will be able to host exchange visitors to Deptford Creek and provide monitoring information on the progress of the project.

The Environment Agency is keen to see this connection as it has international partners for river restoration projects and these can be part of the network that is created. The EA is already using Deptford Creek as an example of good practice in partnership regeneration of tidal watercourses.

Young Citizens' Conference
July 1996

Recognising that young people have their own views about the area they live in, the Creek Project organised a one-day young citizens' conference. The University of Greenwich contributed free use of their lecture theatre and teaching rooms for workshops. Two local primary schools sent over 80 delegates. The day involved an introductory session, a site visit, and workshops on boating and heritage, the natural environment, the built environment, and planning the future. Two delegates from each workshop reported back to the main conference using microphones and a range of suitable props.

young citizens bring a different perspective

London Borough of Lewisham

The children brought a completely different perspective, surprising even those adults who regularly work with schoolchildren. The only criticism from teachers was a lack of summary material for follow-up work. The experience has directly influenced the Groundwork in Education programme in establishing the Creekside Schools Network, and helped confirm the need for the Floating Education Centre.

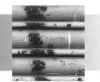

Barrages
Contributing to regional and international debate

Barrages continue to be a topical issue. They are often proposed for visual enhancement reasons yet the build up of silt behind them can look worse than the original situation. The environmental impacts can be devastating.

The new Cardiff Bay barrage has apparently run into operational problems and is not yet working. The Wandle half-tide weir has caused numerous problems. The Barking barrage has recently been constructed and monitoring has been agreed for the future to assess the true effects on tidal water quality and the local environment.

Internationally barrages remain the subject of great debate. It is recognised that the Deptford Creek solution provides a valuable alternative design for comparison. The monitoring of its enhancements over time will provide important data for future designs elsewhere.

Wandsworth Challenge Partnership
Swapping stories between boroughs

Wandsworth Challenge Partnership is dealing with a similar situation at Bell Lane Creek. The Creek Environment project manager was invited to to give a slide talk to the Wandsworth Society in 1997. Through word-of-mouth links we decided to meet up and share experiences when Wandsworth were successful in their Challenge Partnership bid.

These informal links are still proving useful. The Creek project can feed back why some approaches have proved effective and others have not. In return, Wandsworth will have some different ideas that we can learn from. Two of the local surveyors from the Creek Project have been commissioned to carry out surveys of Bell Lane Creek. The flora survey has already shown that there are a number of interesting differences between the two tidal creeks. For instance Bell Lane Creek supports no saltmarsh species. In compensation it does have a greater variety of freshwater plants such as marsh ragwort and pink water speedwell. This highlights the importance of detailed local surveys. Each stretch of the Thames and its tributaries is variable and locally distinct.

where are we now?

The initial consultants' work, the volume of ecological surveying, the public meetings and project planning meetings have all taken place over a period of two years and eight months. The role that the project has taken on in using this information to comment on designs proposed by local developers, the Environment Agency and potential schemes still in the pipeline has taken time that could have been used in progressing 'our own work'.

However, the decision was made that while an early result would have come out of such methodology, it would have been implemented in isolation. Other site designs would not have complemented ours and the original vision of a partnership regenerating and enhancing the wildlife value and amenity of the Creek would not have been fulfilled. Construction designs are one of the last stages in the process not the first.

We know that our designs will be based on the findings of the surveys and that, as other developments come on stream, we are able to offer detailed advice as to how they can conserve and enhance the life and legacy of Deptford Creek. Last but not least, we know that everyone locally has had a chance to comment so that implementation can go forward without delay and with popular support.

It would make a pleasant change to be able to end on an upbeat note for London's wild environments. However, despite the increasing use of buzzwords like sustainability and biodiversity, when it comes to urban environments it seems any optimism is unfounded. Two current Government initiatives are likely to accelerate the impact on London's wildlife. These are the 'Sustainability Counts' indicators and the Urban Task Force.

The Government is in the process of devising a set of criteria to assess sustainable development in the UK. One of the proposed indicators is the proportion of development on brownfield sites as opposed to greenfield sites. To date the whole debate surrounding greenfield vs brownfield sites has been simplistic and ignorant. It is the latest form of colour prejudice; these are not qualitative terms. Greenfields come in a variety of guises: some are the most important sites for wildlife in the country, the majority, however, are not. The green fields of Britain have been devastated by sixty years of intensive industrial agriculture.

In contrast, brownfield sites contain some of London's most important wildlife habitats. A recent audit of sites of nature conservation importance by the London Wildlife Trust found that more than a quarter of them are on brownfield sites. This amounts to over 4,000 hectares of land. Using the new indicator, building on all of these would be called 'sustainable development'.

The recent Urban Task Force interim report *Urban Renaissance* is even more worrying. It devotes less than a page to the environment. The report highlights one consultee as stating that building on brownfield sites, which he acknowledges are better for wildlife, is a 'win/win situation'. Of the 25 Key Principles to Emerge from the Consultation Process not one mentions the wild environment at all. Currently it seems likely that when the 'new vision for urban regeneration' is published it will target wildlife habitats on brownfield sites.

At present in urban areas the wildflower of time is facing the grim reaper of destiny.

There will be an important threshold at the end of the SRB-funded Creek Environment Project as we move towards an independent Friends of Deptford Creek. At that moment it will be essential to review all the work undertaken within the Creek and we intend to produce a short update to this publication, to illustrate the local impact of Creekside renewal.

sources & index

local profiles

We chose six interested local residents and asked them to tell us what Creekside means to them.....

Dusty Gedge

I live in Greenwich. The Creek is a boundary. On the other side of the boundary is Deptford. That other place I never went to. I passed through it on the train or on the No 53. I might even have given it a cursory glance from the river bus, but I had no reason to stop. Now I do. All this Creek business has introduced me to a whole new world.

The other thing about boundaries is that they are wonderful places. Especially for birds. And birds do it for me. And in this muddy borderland I've seen loads. Oh! Not as many as you would see at some top birding spot out there in the country. But out there have you got all that lovely 'ugliness'? No. Now, don't get me wrong, a stroll along the Thames at Teddington is a top idea, but I don't live there. So a stroll along the Creek is as good as it gets. And by golly it can be quite good. Peer over the wall at Booker's, feast your eyes on all that mud and you might, just might, get a glimpse of a kingfisher. Wow! In the middle of all this humanity and humanity's mess the nation's favourite bird is doing its thing. On a bleeding shopping trolley. Gets me every time.

Now I know birds are my bag but since I got involved in this Creek business I've discovered other things too. I've tickled a flounder whilst wearing PVC waders! Ummm. I've been the helmsman of a boat which for a landlubber like me is a bit of a thrill. A very hairy man has described the virtues of certain rare lichens and mosses doing their thing on dilapidated river walls. I've even sat around tables with men and women in suits and had clandestine meetings about gabions and steel trusses. Technical stuff, eh! But best of all, yes best of all, I have discovered a little avian anarchist who struts his stuff where many would prefer him not to be strutting at all. And all this on the boundary of SE8 and SE10.

Rev. Graham Corneck

I have only been in Deptford for 25 years. The Creek began its life-transforming work shortly after God said: "let the world begin". Take a few million years and gently let a river flow into another river and in time a hole will be dug. A hole, a trench and depth that is deeper than round about. So when Henry VIII wanted to build his navy he found in Deptford the shipbuilding skills that had grown up over the years and started his naval expansion here. As Deptford Broadway was embracing Watling Street, so the Creek provided a need for a bridge and in its turn a strategic point for tolls and battles against invaders and grand processions for monarchs returning from foreign exploits.

The tide was a 22ft tide that added to commercial possibilities of bigger and bigger ships and boats being able to use the asset of the Creek. Before the roads and railways came, the easiest form of transport was by water. Smooth, steady and reliable. Look at an old map of the Creek and see how many mills you can count. All these were served with grain and carried the wheat and flour, when ground, to all over the county. With the Creek, Deptford had a motorway before they were a twinkle in anyone's eye.

Now, with so much change happening along both banks of the Creek, and the waterway itself being treated with the care it deserves, the Creek will take on a new meaning and a leisure significance that will be a wonder to all who can afford to live here! Our wondrous educators in things environmental – flowers, fauna and ferns – bless us with an abundance of opportunities to become aware of the beauty secretly nourished among us and now through redevelopment to be revealed. Deptford is a joy and a jewel of a town. The Creek is the silver ribbon that shines from its brow.

Bill Ellson

Mud. No picture postcard this place. A few bits of green, the odd duck. A man explains, plants I've never heard of, fish that I did not know were there. An old map is passed round, long gone gasworks, manufacturing industry. All a long time ago. I recall an ancient newspaper, 1850 I think though maybe '51. "The most polluted waterway in England" or was it Britain? I can't recall but I share my knowledge anyway. That sounds about right, all agree. I ask more questions, answers come from young and old. ARE THERE SWANS? Laughter reigns as a majestic flotilla turns from the Thames and commences its regal progress upstream. We begin our walk. I am not to know the journey I am beginning, but the pilgrimage started there, that day. The walk: old walls, new walls, scraped walls, dropwort, graffiti and much, much more. The walk ends. This is the Theatre Arm. I excitedly tell of sunbathing ducklings the summer before.

Come to a meeting. A tentative invite. But perhaps I already know that I am hooked. I must go. I will go. I do go. Pete Pope is there, but no others I know. Loads of paper. How does this relate to the revelations of the walk? Time for coffee comes, my naïve questions are answered. Another meeting. Shall I go? I go to Creek Bridge at 1am. Or was it 2? My question is answered. I go again. A break. I join the other pariahs outside for a cigarette.

The discussions filled that night. I feel part of the meeting. More papers. The jigsaw takes shape. As one survey illuminates the previous one, and the next one, so the Creek seems wider and deeper each nocturnal visit. Slowly the rhythms of the tide, and Prior's, and Booker's, and ducks and geese, reveal themselves. The Creek quietly seeps into my bones. I know so many names now, of people, of plants, of birds, of wharves and developers. I know, I feel the life of the Creek. Timeless and eternal. Changing yet the same. No place for preservation just because it's old. Change will come. The Creek can cope but respect its life and know that it lives. No picture postcard this place, but for those who take time to watch, listen, read and share, a greater revelation waits.

Portia Smith

There are three stages to learning to love Deptford Creek. The first starts with total lack of knowledge. You can walk the streets of sunny Deptford without ever coming across this special hidden waterway. You might glimpse it on the way home from the Bird's Nest or stand on the road bridge and wonder where it comes from, where it goes, but you don't really notice it. You don't take it in.

Then something happens. For me I got a job. Other people I have met came to it by other means. Strange people talking at public meetings, at public houses or just in the street. There is something special about the water. I suppose it's the assumption that nothing of value lives there. People have the same attitude towards Deptford. Surprised that Deptford has award-winning restaurants, beautiful architecture, art galleries, incredible history, and people who care about it. In the same way this book will show that the Creek has crabs and flounders, carp and eels, herons, shrimps and nematodes.

What changes is not what you look at but how you look. The mud is just mud till you know what's in it. It's wriggling with life. In a world where money increasingly come first, it is nice that someone is doing something to save the things that don't earn. Maybe we should employ the creatures; get the cormorants fishing for us; train the crabs to clear rubbish; educate the shrimps in the complexity of quarterly returns. And now the Creek is part of my surroundings. When I go past it or over I stop to look at the tides, see if I can catch a glimpse of the elusive kingfishers. I grew up in the countryside and spent many hours stomping around in wild spaces. The Creek is a wild space and thanks to Jill's work it will remain so.

Patrick and Parfaite Wilson

I met my love on the London-bound platform
Where the wild grasses grow over the
carriage ramp;
We dream our dreams looking out
Over the Creek Road Bridge at dusk,
Watching the ducks feed in the mud
And this dirty old Deptford is the place where
we love.

Parfaite writes: When I left my country I went to Paris and then London. I lived in different areas, studying English and working. One day my cousin took me shopping in Deptford Market. I really liked the feeling of Deptford and in 1996 I got a room in the co-op flats behind the station. Soon after that, I met Patrick. We spend a lot of our free time walking around the area. Creekside is quiet and peaceful. We enjoy going to the river and just observing what is there. I am not so interested in politics, but Deptford is my home now so I want it to be a place where we can live and enjoy.

Patrick writes: Creekside is a new name for an old familiar place. Three years ago I came back to live here, drawn by family ties and fragments of childhood memory which add up to a sense of belonging. I have met new friends and of course Parfaite who is now my wife. Deptford has changed a lot over the decades and it seems the agents of regeneration are keen to continue their well-intentioned efforts to improve our lot. I think it is an important to understand the processes which affect our environment. If this book can give a perspective on where we are, and a glimpse of where we might be heading, then it will be a valuable guide to all of us who want to survive and thrive on Creekside.

Bridget Perry

The thing people don't understand is that water is dangerous, but it's only dangerous if you abuse it. The adventure playground can be dangerous if the kids abuse it. It is just the same with the river. They get to an age and you have to let them be responsible for themselves, which builds a mutual trust between you. We should educate kids how to use the river and the parents as well. All you get is "Don't go near the river!" Mine have been going down there for years. It's one of the cheapest ways of entertaining kids. Hannah has brought stones home, painted them and kept them. Simple things that don't take a lot of working out. I remember years ago if anyone fell in the river they went into hospital for 24 hours automatically. My kids have paddled in that river for years and at Deptford Green when the tide is up, the bigger kids used to dive off the jetty.

I think the Creek should be made more accessible to the people that live here. A lot of young kids would love to get down there and explore with properly qualified people, if they could do pond dipping and identify what they have caught, a shrimp or a crab. I think the environment education centre is a really good thing for all the schools in the area.

They moan about the lorries but they've got a river there. Why don't they use it? Its got to be the easiest, least polluted form of transport. I'd like to see more work on the Creek in terms of usage and transport. There's a gravel firm that use the river. They should stay but maybe they won't fit in with the image of the Creek. The developers just think water, land, money.

I feel all of a sudden it's a view that will only benefit the people who can afford to live right on the edge of it. I just hope it doesn't turn into yuppie land. Surrey Quays is like a ghost town during the day because they are all out at work, earning money to pay their fabulous mortgages.

I think with the physical renewal it will be lovely over there. People say 'it will be so nice not to see those scrapyards' but they kept people alive for years, they were bread and butter, not just for the people that worked there. If you needed a part for your car that's where you'd get it. All that is going. I know there's progress but the whole history of the power station, it's just gone. It's crazy. They're building a bandstand. That's what they did at the turn of the last century; built bandstands everywhere in the parks. I don't know a brass band in Deptford. We should start one up, get them to play there, just to see the reaction!

Jim Rice

In the early 1990s Ilford Photographer of the Year Jim Rice began taking photographs of the Creek Mouth area with its "dying industrial landscape" as it "awaits the end of the recession and the hand of the developer".

Alongside many excellent portraits of the welders, scrappies and aggregate workers are a series dramatically documenting the demolition of Deptford Power Station. The selection of Jim's photographs published by Cornerhouse and the Museum of London in 1993 captured "an image of Deptford Creek that will shortly be lost"...

sources

Surveys commissioned by the Creek Environment Project are marked with an asterisk.

legacy sources

Bold, John & Guillery, Peter	"Historical Assessment of Suburbs" *Urban Design Quarterly*, April 1998
Building Conservation Design	*Wood Wharf: A Life Preserver for the Working Thames* [March 1997]
* Canty, Mike	*Rubbish Survey* [1998]
Deptford into the 80s	*Up The Creek: 250 years of Deptford People and Places* [1980]
Dews, Nathan	*History of Deptford* [1884, reprinted 1972]
English Heritage	*Sustaining the historic environment: new perspectives on the future* [1997]
* Gaimster, Drs David & Märit	*Excavations on Deptford Broadway 1989 & 1992: reassessment of artefactual evidence* [1998]
Gill, Brian	*Deptford and its Dockyards: an archaeological survey* [1998]
Goldsmiths College Industrial Archaeology Group	*Industrial Archaeology of South East London* [1982]
* Museum of London Archaeology Service	*An Archaeological Foreshore Survey for the Creekside Project* [July 1997]
* Phillpotts, Dr Chris	*Deptford Creek. Archaeological Desk-based Assessment* [August 1997]
Pre-Construct Archaeology	*Lower Watergate and Foreshore desktop assessment* [August 1996]
Pre-Construct Archaeology	*Greenwich Reach Development desktop assessment* [April 1994]
Prockter, Adrian	*London & Greenwich Railway 150th anniversary* [1986]
RCHME	*No 1-31 (odd) Tanners Hill, Deptford* [1998]
RCHME	*Deptford Houses: 1650 to 1800* [1998]
Rice, Jim	*Deptford Creek (photographs)* [1993]
Spurgeon, Darrell	*Discover Deptford and Lewisham* [1997]
Steele, Jess	*Turning the Tide: The History of Everyday Deptford* [1993]
Steele, Jess (editor)	*The Streets of London: The Booth Notebooks. Volume 1 South East* [1997]
Walker, Richard	*An Interpretative Plan: St Paul's and Crossfields* [1996]

life of the creek sources

* Archer, John	*Deptford Creek Bird Monitoring: 1996-1997* [April 1997]
British Trust for Ornithology	*Site Action Plan for Black Redstarts in the Deptford Creek Area* [Dec 1997]
Burton, Rodney	*Flora of the London Area* [1983]
* Conservation Works	*The Thin Green Line (flora survey)* [January 1999]
Creek Environment Project	*Black redstarts of Deptford Creek* [July 1998]
Environment Agency	*River Ravensbourne Fisheries Survey* [1996]
Environment Agency	*Fish Found in the Tidal Thames*
Environment Agency	*Invertebrate Animals of the Tidal Thames*
Environment Agency	*Ravensbourne & Marsh Dykes Local Environment Agency Plan* [Dec 1997]
* Gedge, Dusty	*Deptford Creek Bird Monitoring: 1997-1998* [April 1998]
Gedge, Dusty	*Black Redstart – A Bird for London* [1998]
* Herbert, Clive	*Deptford Creek Bat Survey* [September 1997]
* Jones, Richard A	*Life on the Edge: Terrestrial Invertebrate Survey of Deptford Creek* [1998]
London Ecology Unit	*Monitoring bird populations on Sites of Nature Conservation Importance in London* [1996]
London Wildlife Trust	*Millennium Domesday: wildlife under threat along the Greenwich waterfront* [July 1998]
London Wildlife Trust	*Wild London. Winter/Spring 1998*
* Massini, Peter	*Deptford Creek: Assessment of Habitats & Proposed Conservation Management for Birds*
McDonagh, Melanie	"Our Brown and Pleasant Land" in *The Spectator*, 14 March 1998
National Rivers Authority	*River Ravensbourne Fisheries Survey* [1991]
* Natural History Museum	*Deptford Creek Algal Survey* [December 1997]
* Paice, Mike	*The Birds of Deptford Creek 1995-1997* [August 1997]
* Physalia Ltd	*The Faunal Communities of Deptford Creek: Two Foreshore Sites* [August 1998]
Unicomarine Ltd	*Deptford Creek Biological Survey (aquatic invertebrates)* [August 1997]
* University of Greenwich	*Biological-Ecological Survey: Aquatic macroinvertebrates in sediments of Deptford Creek*
* University of Greenwich	*Chemical Survey. Strategy 1: site-specific assessment and Strategy 2: Creek-wide survey*

renewal sources

Babtie Group — *Deptford Creek Flood Defence Options. Preliminary Report* [April 1997]

Babtie Group — *Reconstruction & Refurbishment Options for Priority Frontages* [Sept 1997]

Babtie Group, Robert West Consulting & Urban Initiatives — *Report for public consultation meeting 30/4/97*

Bott, Val & Taylor, Alison — *A Guide to Education and the Thames*

Centre for Urban & Community Research — *Case Studies in Urban Regeneration in Creekside SRB Partnership* [July 1998]

Centre for Urban & Community Research — *The Urban Regeneration Process in Creekside SRB Partnership* [July 1998]

Centre for Urban & Community Research — *Community Involvement in Creekside SRB Partnership* [July 1998]

Creekside Partnership — *Creekside Renewal: Building Bridges. SRB bid* [September 1995]

Creekside Renewal SRB — *Annual Report 1996/97 & Annual Report 1997/98*

Deptford Discovery Team — *Deptford Creek Life (leaflet/poster for Creek Environment Project)* [1998]

Deptford Discovery Team — *The Deptford Discovery & Ha'penny Hatch Walk proposal* [Oct 1994]

Deptford Discovery Team — *The Deptford Discovery & Ha'penny Hatch Walk & Cycle Route: feasibility study* [Oct 1995]

Deptford Discovery Team — *Revealing the Waterfront (millennium lottery bid)* [November 1996]

* Deptford Discovery Team — *Creekside Education Strategy: Review of Research & Projects to Date* [July 1998]

Deptford Discovery Team — *A Trip Through Deptford* [1997]

Deptford Discovery Team — *Introduction to Groundwork's Vital Centres & Green Links Deptford Creek Programme* [1997]

* Deptford Forum Publishing — *Creekside Surveys Publication: Stage 1 Study* [May 1997]

Docklands Forum & Greenwich Waterfront Community Forum — *Millennium: Partnerships for Sustainable Regeneration* [1996]

Environment Agency — *Wandle Basin Options Study* [1997]

Environment Agency — *The Tidal Foreshore* [no date]

Environment Agency — *Partnership in Planning: riverbank design guidance for the Tidal Thames* [1997]

Environment Agency — *The Riverside Owners Guide*

Environmental Council — *Local Environmental Information Centres: an overview*

* GAP Research — *Possible Uses and Potential Users of the Creekside Interpretation Centre* [Oct 1997]

Government Office for London — *Thames Strategy: Strategic Planning & Design Guidance* [April 1995]

Greenwich Agenda 21 — *Local Agenda 21 strategy for sustainable development in Greenwich* [1997]

Greenwich Engineering & Property Management — *Ha'penny Hatch Bridge Options Report* [January 1997]

Lee, Trisha & Breadin, Tim — *The Asphalt Desert: an Environmental Audit of Creekside Schools* [September 1997]

London Boroughs of Greenwich & Lewisham — *Creekside Strategy: joint regeneration initiative for Deptford Creek* [Nov 1993]

London Borough of Greenwich — *Greenwich Waterfront Strategy* [1991]

London Rivers Association — *A Study of River- Dependent Industry in Greenwich & Lewisham* [Feb 1995]

London Rivers Association — *The Thames- side Safety Study: a guide to good practice* [Feb 1992]

Magpie Resource Library — *The Regeneration Experience* [1998]

National Rivers Authority — *Ravensbourne Catchment Landscape Assessment* [May 1992]

* Robert West Consulting — *Deptford Creek River Walls & Channel Bed Environmental Enhancement Designs* [Sept 1997]

Robert West Consulting — *Greenwich Reach Development. Deptford Creek River Walls Condition Survey* [Jan 1996]

Robert West Consulting — *Deptford Power Station Landing Stage Condition Survey & Review of Options for Development (for Deptford Discovery Team)* [Sept 1996]

Social Exclusion Unit — *Bringing Britain together: a national strategy for neighbourhood renewal* [Sept 1998]

Steele, Jess — *Creekside Communications Strategy* [July 1998] commissioned by the Creekside Forum

Thames Explorer Trust — *Investigating the Foreshore of the River Thames* [1997]

Timpson Manley — *Creekside Masterplan for the environs of the new Laban Centre London* [Oct 1998]

W S Atkins Consultants Ltd — *Deptford Creek Study. Stage 1: Options for Creek, Barrage or Tidal?* [Oct 1994]

W S Atkins Consultants Ltd — *Deptford Creek Study. Stage 2: Environmental Enhancements* [Oct 1995]

* Urban Initiatives — *Creekside Land Use, Access & Recreation Strategy* [July 1997]

Urban Initiatives — *St Paul's Area Study* [July 1994]

Urban Task Force — *Urban Renaissance: Sharing the Vision* [Jan 1999]

Some of the surveyors provided written comments on other surveys and these are available at the Creekside Project Office.

Archive copies of the monthly community newspaper, the Deptford Kite, are held at Magpie Resource Library. A number of issues of the Kite included articles about Creekside.

index